A Year on our Farm

Ann & Robin Talbot

To Sarah and Ruth,
the joys of our lives

and to Rachel
always in our hearts

ISBN: 978-0-9551929-3-7

First published by Laois Education Publishing (LEP)
Coliseum Lane, Portlaoise, Co. Laois.
Email: laoised@eircom.net

The publishers have taken every care to ensure that the information contained in this book is correct but cannot be held responsible for the consequences of any inaccuracies. If any errors or omissions are drawn to the publisher's attention every effort will be made to correct these in future editions.

Designed & Printed by **PRINT***central, Portlaoise, Co. Laois*

CONTENTS

Foreword

There is a tendency to romanticise farming in the popular press, when very often farming is less than romantic. "A year on our Farm" by Ann & Robin Talbot is a lovely story about the ordinary routine on a less than ordinary farm. It is large by Irish standards and opens its gates to several hundred visitors a year. Yet it is deeply traditional, a family farm.

This is a story of seasons and the unseasonal! Of farm yard and farm house. Of the people who are part of the farming calendar and how, while things rarely change they never stay the same.

I know Ann and Robin Talbot for some time now. They are a very special couple devoted to each other and their children and committed to their community. In the pages of this book we see the workings of the farm over a twelve-month period.

The book tells stories of the townland of Ballacolla in Co Laois. Best of all are the accounts of the everyday normal farming routine, including wildlife on the farm and their comings and goings. And the photographs are fantastic.

So too are the descriptions, of simple pleasures - well fed and well bedded cattle and young calves bucking and galloping!

But bad things happen too, where there are livestock there will be dead stock, despite the best efforts of the farmer and diseases hit and hurt, as the book records.

Ann's description of the colour of the cattle and the explanation as to why their animals are "a fairly mongrel bunch" is a crash course in

bovine genetics.

I applaud the section about the farm office and the downside of doing office work in the evening or at night - a good recipe for frustration and an even better one for mistakes! The description of "shoebox syndrome" will ring true on so many farms; women will especially understand this one.

The harsh financial realities of farming, even or especially on a large very productive farm, are clearly spelt out and should be read by those who fail to understand why public money is needed to keep livestock farming alive. Robin's chapter on the EU and farming I have read twice! I only wish I could persuade

the experts in the EU Commission and some environmental organisations that farmers are doing very positive things for the environment without being forced to, but because they want to.

Farms are places where people come and go. Vets, contractors, advisers and specialists. On the Talbot farm their presence is important and valued. It is the part of farming life which I especially like and admire.

I laughed when I read the chapter "Our breakfast" and "Their breakfast" recipes!

And I very much enjoyed the recipes which Ann has shared with us, including her meticulous preparation to have the aroma of hot scones filling the house in the early morning. One very good reason to pay a long overdue visit.

Mairéad McGuinness MEP

Introduction

On behalf of the Talbot family I would like to welcome you to our farm and to this book, a broadly chronological account of what happened over a 12-month period in 2012 on our suckler farm in Coole, Ballacolla, Co Laois, where we produce beef cattle for the domestic and export markets.

The book records the day-to-day operations on the frm over the course of 2012 and hopefully this will be of interest to other farmers. My husband, Robin Talbot, and I also hope that the many consumers who care very much about where their food comes from will learn a little bit more about farming and the food production process. When farmers are in the spotlight it is often because of some crisis, financial, social, environmental or otherwise but there is a whole other side to farming which is both positive and progressive; and while we get plenty stick for our willingness and ability to fight our corner, the reality is that most farmers spend more them agitating slurry than agitating politically.

Robin is the fourth generation Talbot to run this farm. He has worked here since leaving school, just after completing his Inter Cert. I, on the other hand, grew up in West Limerick and worked for almost 20 years as an agricultural journalist for various publications including the *Farming Independent* and *Farm Exam* under my maiden name, Fitzgerald.

We met in January 2000 when I was reporting on the famous Portlaoise meeting that kick-started the so-called Beef War, and we married in 2002. I was aged 38 at the time, Robin 45,

making us late starters in the marriage stakes, so we were very lucky to be able to have a family, Rachel (devastatingly stillborn at term in 2003), followed by Sarah in 2004 and Ruth in 2007, the latter achievement of which definitely qualifies me as a "gummy mummy"!*

With a few obvious exceptions, all of the photographs featured here were taken on the farm. I am not a trained photographer, however. I am merely an energetic member of the spray-and-pray brigade who has tried to capture farm events as they happened in 2012 – the births and deaths, splendours and hardships. I have also tried to create photographic portraits of some of the people who contribute to the successful running of this substantial enterprise.

Our holding comprises some 235 hectares. While this does not represent an average farm size in Ireland, the activities that take place here are, I believe, representative of everyday life on farms all over the island of Ireland.

Our core objective is to make a comfortable living for our family while simultaneously ensuring that the activities we engage in do not have a negative impact on the environment.

With the exception of a few orphan calves or an occasional stock bull, our cattle are rarely referred to by name. Instead, they are identified by their tag number, colour, build and perhaps personality – especially those that are inclined to be high-spirited. Irrespective of their temperament, however, we treat every animal respectfully. We love our cattle and while they may not have a long life here in Coole at least they have a contented existence where they always have enough to eat and

drink as well as somewhere dry to lie down when they want to rest.

Robin and I know we are privileged and blessed in having a sufficient selection of the wholesome ingredients that allow us to create a happy life: a robust marriage; two lovely, healthy children; good friends; a nice home in a picturesque rural setting – all of this coupled with the spirit, body and opportunity to make a decent living.

That said, we face endless challenges, not least the fact that the future of commercial beef farming is up in the air as a consequence of current CAP reform. As in all reforms, there will be winners and losers and we won't know where we stand until we see the fine print.

In the interim, the next time a housewife (or house husband) who has read this book visits their butcher, perhaps they will arrive there armed with a keener understanding of the farmer's role in getting beef from conception to consumption, coupled with a deeper knowledge of the hard work, joy, pride and perpetual passion that such an undertaking entails.

And so begins my account of life in Coole during 2012. I hope you enjoy reading it as much as we enjoyed writing it.

Ann Talbot
July, 2013

*My term, for those who become mums at an older age, many of us, including myself actually have quite good teeth.

Stone sign approaching the village from the direction of Durrow.

The River Erkina floods the Curraghs.

A pair of Mute swans swim up the River Gully with the Slieve Blooms in the distance.

Ballacolla village.

Location

For those of you who have never visited Co Laois, it is located in the centre of Ireland. Because its landscapes are less dramatic than those found elsewhere in Ireland, "Lovely Laois" doesn't often feature on Irish tourist maps. Nonetheless, it is truly a fine county, physically and socially, as well as a great place to live, work and visit.

In addition to the Slieve Blooms – which although smaller, are as beautiful as any of the country's better-known mountains – Co Laois has many fine woods and walks, including Dunmore, Bishopswood, Killamuck Bog in Abbeyleix, the Leafy Loops in Durrow and Grantstown Wood.

Nearby attractions for families and other visitors include the agricultural museum in Donaghmore, the heritage centre in Abbeyleix and, a little further afield, the Rock of Dunamaise, Emo Court and Lough Boora, just over the border in Co Offaly.

Thanks to the M7 and M8 motorways, Dublin, Cork and Limerick and a range of shopping and cultural amenities are all little more than an hour away. Closer to home is the town of Portlaoise, with its excellent Dunamaise Theatre. The city of Kilkenny and the towns of Carlow and Thurles also have a number of good cultural and entertainment venues.

Laois has most types of land – ranging from very fertile to mountainous to boggy – and almost three cattle per person (i.e. a total of 230,000 animals versus 80,000 people).

Our farm in Coole is situated on a wedge of generally good agricultural land in the southern reaches of the county, sandwiched between the Gully and the Erkina, just before both rivers join the Nore. The Curragh or locally Curraghs, is a 600 acre flood plain of the Erkina, which attracts large numbers of waders and waterfowl, including Lapwing, Golden Plover, Mallard, Teal, Shoveler and Curlew. So, while Laois may be Ireland's most landlocked county, this little corner is quite a special place to anyone who is interested in nature, especially birdwatchers.

The farm is located on the outskirts of the picturesque village of Ballacolla. While this is the spelling most commonly used today, there are several other variations, including Ballycallagh (according to the 1655 Down Survey), and Ballycolla (the spelling used in a 1659 census). In 1838 it was recorded in the *Ordnance Survey Parish Namebook* as both Ballacolla and Baile Cholla. The latter name would suggest that it means 'Colla's town' but this is rejected by William Carrigan, who published the seminal *History and Antiquities of the Diocese of Ossory* in 1905. In that book he refers to it as Ballycolla.

The official Irish translation is Bollincholla, i.e. Baile a Chalaidh – the town of the Callow. According to William Carrigan, "this word Callow is in common use in the Queen's County to designate the long, coarse sedging grass thrown up during the summer by land covered over by water all the winter. Callow was abundant in the west part of Ballacolla in the memory of old people recently passed away. Dr Joyce's explanation of Ballacolla viz town of a man named Colla is incorrect."

While the period that William Carrigan is referring to here is likely to have been the early 1800s, there remain significant areas to the east of Ballacolla village which in winter months often lie under floodwater from tributaries of the River Gully. The area is also characterised by another seam of low-lying land to the north and west of the townland which has been largely drained. Two hundred years ago, the wetness would have been more extensive, stretching towards the boundaries of Kilminfoyle and Tentore in Loughabarra.

A hackneyed hack would undoubtedly call Ballacolla "sleepy" but in fact it is a pretty, vibrant little village, a consistent high performer in the Tidy Towns competition at local and national level, and home (jointly with neighbouring village Clough) to a good senior hurling team. Ballacolla also sprang to national attention in 1995 when it was selected as the venue for the National Ploughing Championships – otherwise known as "The Ploughing", the biggest annual event in the Irish agricultural calendar.

Held partly on our land, the Ploughing returned here in 2000. It was set to be the venue again in 2001 but the event had to be cancelled because of the island's foot-and-mouth disease (FMD) crisis. So, instead, it came back again in 2002.

Ballacolla has to be one of the very few villages in Ireland that did not acquire a new housing estate during the Celtic Tiger years. But, because it sits at the crossroads of the busy R434 and R433 regional roads less than 4km from Junction 3 of the M8 motorway, the area attracts plenty of road traffic. Notable landmarks in the village include three pubs, an agricultural co-op, a modern community centre, a busy corner shop and even a set of quick-changing traffic lights!

Our farm

Our farm is relatively large. It is also well established and has a low level of borrowings. As such, in Irish terms it would be considered quite successful.

In terms of day-to-day help, we have one full-time person, Joe Hyland, who works alongside my husband Robin six and a half days a week. We also take on an agricultural college student for three months every year at calving time. All other work on the farm is carried out by various contractors.

The farm is laid out in three main blocks. So, as for many fragmented holdings, travel adds to the time input required to run the farm. The fragmented layout also adds to the overall amount of work involved. But we consider ourselves lucky because our outfarms are located relatively close to each other.

One block of land runs along a ridge at the back of the village, beside the Rathdowney Road in the townland of Ballacolla: this is adjacent to the main part of the farm, in Coole (which means "back" or "side" in Irish). As a descriptor, the name doesn't sound exciting but it is apt: the land slopes gently from Simon's Hill across the Durrow Road, passing the house and farmyard before rising slightly to the east and north to Coolderry Lane, and from there, past the old Killermogh churchyard to the banks of the River Gully.

The Gully also bounds the outfarm in Ballygeehin (4km from our house). Much of this outfarm is low-lying and while the land is mainly used for pasture we did manage to successfully grow barley on a hillside in Ballygeehin in 2012.

Our other outfarm is to the west, at Tentore (2.5km from home). Robin's late father, Bob Talbot, bought this farm in the late 1940s; since he took over the day-to-day running of the operation Robin has done a lot of work on draining and reclaiming the land. Unfortunately, however, much of the soil is heavy and, in addition, the section of the holding in Loughabarra includes about 30 acres of wet grassland.

Ours is a single enterprise, focused on breeding and rearing beef cattle. Except for our six horses (a mare and foal, three youngstock and one fat pony which are very definitely a hobby rather than a commercial activity, as they only ever cost us money), we grow some crops, maize silage (occasionally) and barley. All of these crops are exclusively designed to service the sucklers – to provide grain for their feed and straw for their bedding.

Our type of farming is quite different from what Robin would have experienced as a child in the 1960s and 1970s – when the farm was (as would have been fairly typical of the period) pretty close to self-sufficient. Back then, his family reared everything from milking cows and fattening cattle to various types of fowl, pigs and sheep. They also grew several crops, including barley, sugar beet, wheat and turnips, and they maintained a good garden that produced a range of fruit and vegetables.

The system

At the heart of our farm today is a herd of 220 suckler cows. These are mostly Limousin, crossed with either a Belgian Blue bull or a Limousin bull, the former producing heavier, more muscled calves, the latter being easier to calve so they are used on heifers.

Like many other animal species, beef calves tend to be born in the spring. This timing works well on most farms because often the calves are either born outdoors or they are turned outdoors shortly after birth.

Fortunately, modern housing and management systems offer other options and, as a result, we have changed our farming practice, moving to calve all our cows in the autumn. This practice would not work for everyone or on all farms but it does for us because it means that all our other stock are feeding themselves outdoors during a period when our cows are calving. As such, it frees up more time for us to devote to the cows and their calves.

Rightly or not, we believe that autumn calving also has the potential to generate more profit. This view is based on the fact that the cattle feed we produce most cheaply in this country is grass.

As the finishing age for beef cattle is sometime between the ages of 18 and 24 months, it means they are likely to spend just one entire summer outdoors. It makes sense that they should be as mature as possible when they reach the outdoor grazing stage – so they are able to eat as much grass as possible. Thus, while it is relatively expensive to house both calves and cows for the duration of the calves' first winter, we believe this expense is more than offset by the better weight gain they achieve during the following grazing season.

In addition, financial returns tend to be greater because beef prices tend to be higher at the time when the cattle are ready for sale. One of the reasons for this is that higher prices are achieved when supplies of stock are tighter – a consequence of the fact that fewer people operate the August/September calving system.

All this means that August and September are the most important months of the year on our farm. Everything we do is about getting as many calves as we can safely delivered. If the August/September period is not successful, nothing we do for the rest of the year will make up for it.

In order to make the job of calving more manageable, we employ a system called night-time feeding. Cows spend the day on a relatively bare field and are then housed at night, at which point they are offered hay. The theory behind night-time feeding is that if the cows' bodies are busy eating and digesting, they don't have time to "think" about calving, and this gets deferred until the more sociable daytime hours so they are easier to observe and manage if intervention is necessary. Also there is less overall interruption to our sleep and that of the vet. In order for the system to work

successfully, however, the night-time feeding regime needs to be introduced at least one month before the cows begin calving.

All the cows approaching calving are kept in one paddock. Then, once the calf has been safely delivered, mother and calf are moved to another, post-calving, paddock. After that, calves have up to the middle of November or thereabouts to harden up, before being moved indoors for the winter months.

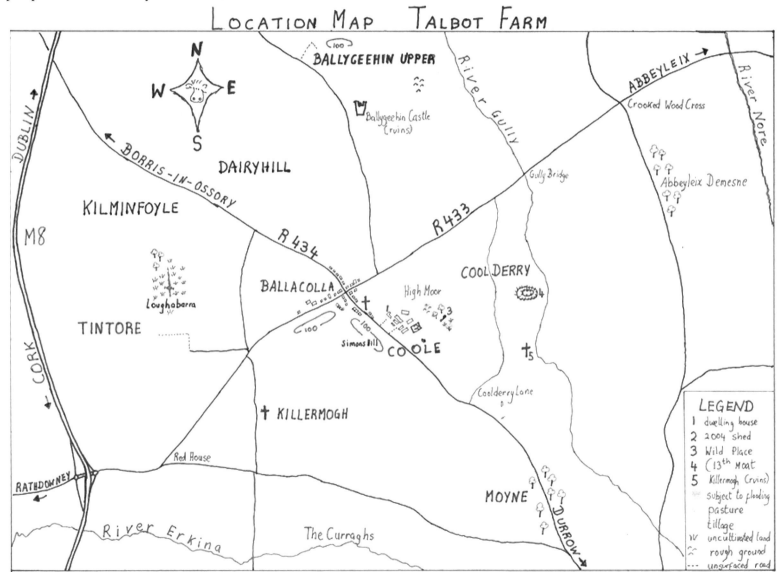

LOCATION MAP   TALBOT FARM

(not to scale)

LEGEND
1 dwelling house
2 2004 shed
3 Wild Place
4 C13th Moat
5 Killermogh (ruins)
∿ subject to flooding
    pasture
    tillage
ᴡ uncultivated land
∼ rough ground
--- unsurfaced road

JANUARY

Spreading dung on the stubbles.

Bums in a row, peas in a pod.

Ruth.

Bull calves play in the winter sunshine.

Beef bull which died from IBR.

David Thompson, plumber, of Ballyroan.

Sarah.

With the strains of "Auld Lang Syne" still lingering in the air, the days visibly lengthen.

The weather is mild and snowdrops are bursting through the grass verges along the avenue. This is lovely, of course, but I can't help feeling that we will pay for it somehow, sometime.

While the grazing fields are surprisingly sticky, the stubbles are dry and we are able to spread dung on the land.

In the yards, everything seems to be going according to plan and it is noticeable that the bull calves, which have access to a field, are spending more time outdoors.

Feeding and bedding

She stepped out and I stepped in again.
I stepped out and she stepped in again.

The feeding and bedding system may not have the fire or frenzy of *Lanigan's Ball* but because it is the most important and time-consuming daily job on our farm during the winter months, it involves a lot of highly choreographed and energetic twisting and turning. It requires two people, Robin and Joe, working three pieces of machinery – loader, feeder wagon and straw blower – in order to feed and bed 600 cattle every day. The task takes up the first two hours of the working day. On the occasions when Robin has to do it on his own, it takes over four hours.

"The first few days, it's like landing a plane on an aircraft carrier, with numerous hand signals transmitted between Joe and myself," says Robin, "but very quickly you develop an understanding of what the other person is doing and where they are headed next. For example, one of us would be starting to bed a shed over the back wall just as the feeder would be finishing filling the trough with feed at the front."

Most of the cattle will be out of the lying areas by now and, in order to ensure that they don't inadvertently inhale dust, any stragglers are also hunted out, the cows to the troughs and the calves to their creep feed area, with the gates shut behind them for the duration of the process.

When the cattle first come indoors in the autumn we make sure that all calves are seen and checked as early as possible during the day – usually after they have been fed. The

TMR tumbles from feeder wagon into trough.

'Lanigan's Ball'.

other batches of stock are then fed, with the cattle on slats fed last. As the latter do not need to be bedded, this frees up one person to attend to some other task.

The cattle are fed a total mixed ration (TMR). This is prepared in a diet feeder which chops and mixes the various ingredients. So precise is the system that the ingredients actually have to be added in a specific order so the ingredients are fully blended. The theory behind this is that the last bite should be the same as the first. This prevents the possibility of a feeding frenzy in which the biggest cattle would inevitably force their way to the trough first and pick out the tastiest ingredients.

In terms of its composition, TMR is similar to the human breakfast cereal and snack food, granola, in that the ingredients used in TMR are "coated". However, while granola may contain oil and a sweetener such as honey or maple syrup, TMR contains molasses. The addition of molasses aids palatability but its prime purpose is to provide a source of energy.

The main components of our cattle's indoor diet are grass silage, home-grown barley,

wheaten straw and elements such as soya (for protein) and maize meal. Specific diets for the various batches of cattle are drawn up by Gerry Giggins, a leading animal nutritionist.

One of the underpinning rules of the diets created by Gerry is that, for growing animals, protein is paramount as it is a critical building block for the body while, for finishing cattle, high-energy foods such as molasses assume increased importance in the daily diet.

Two things that Robin is mindful of are the importance of feeding every animal every day, and not giving them double every second day. He also ensures that the order of feeding is the same each day. "Otherwise, they start to get restless. This is not because they're hungry. Rather, it's as if they are afraid they have been forgotten."

On the subject of putting down a bed, Robin says that, this is now a relatively easy job. Until 2004 or thereabouts, the system we operated involved manually bedding every shed every day, using a total of five round bales per day. Weighing around 200kg, the bales are actually cylindrical in shape and measure 1.2 metre high with a diameter of 1.2m. The bedding process involved the loader dropping a bale at

Loading the feeder wagon.

one end of the shed and when it was unrolled (a bit like a Swiss roll without the jam!) the straw was shaken out by fork.

These days, we use a straw blower. This can accommodate two bales which are usually placed in it using the teleporter. Then, the moving floor feeds the bales into a rotating drum where high-speed blades rip the straw out of the bale. This is then fed onto a large flywheel which, using considerable pressure, expels the straw through a chute. The angle of the chute is controlled by a joystick and the straw is sprayed in various directions, up to a distance of 12m, allowing us to cover a large floor space with a loose, fresh layer of bedding in the shortest time possible.

While we classify these as mundane tasks – because they have to be done every day – Robin freely admits that nothing satisfies him more than to see a line of cows with their heads stuck in the trough gleefully filling their tummies while their calves race into the golden straw in the shed behind them for a buck and a gallop.

Simple pleasures!

Visit of the Whooper swans

It is almost a century since WB Yeats wrote his poem about the wild swans at Coole, Co

Galway. Coincidentally, these beautiful creatures are also regular visitors to our Coole.

For the uninitiated, the variety of swan most often seen in Ireland is the Mute, which is commonly seen on lakes, rivers and canals as well as in public parks and some coastal areas. Our visitors are Whoopers (pronounced hooper) which come here during the winter months from their breeding grounds in Iceland – how often do you hear of visitors coming to Ireland to experience better weather! While their normal diet consists of aquatic vegetation, Birdwatch Ireland notes that, sightings of Whoopers feeding on pastureland are being increasingly recorded.

For the past number of years, Whoopers have been arriving at Coole in their hundreds, usually opting for the same field near the area that our daughters have dubbed "the wild place" – a wet and wooded spot north of the farmyard. Because the area is sheltered, Robin always sets it aside for early grass – a practice the Whoopers are well aware of.

On one of the days in January when I went to photograph them while they were grazing, they suddenly took off in a big loop formation, only to land shortly afterwards on the High Moor, within view of the house, much to Robin's (affected) chagrin. "It's bad enough knowing that they're out there eating and dirtying my nice grass. Now, thanks to you they've found another field to do it in and I have to look at them while they're doing it!"

Their arrival date varies. Some years it's as early as October – which is regarded as a sign of cold weather approaching. Other years they may not arrive until January.

small aircraft until you suddenly hear their characteristic sonorous whoop – a sound that is so different from any other sound you are likely to hear on an Irish farm.

Swans are surely one of nature's true, mysterious and imperious splendours. A welcome beacon of beauty in winter, their departure is an equally welcome sign of the approach of spring.

The Whoopers are powerful birds and, during the 'season', they fly in early every morning from their overnight roosts (probably in the Curraghs about 1km away) in a V-shaped formation, honking hauntingly. Once they have finished grazing for the day, they depart at dusk with a similarly evocative display.

Although they have very different lifestyles, the paths of the Mutes and the Whoopers *(see picture previous page)* do cross from time to time. The two are easily distinguishable. The Mute is much larger and has an orange-coloured upper bill; the Whooper's bill is yellow and black, with the yellow section protruding below the nostril.

Even if swans were not a protected species, it is hard to see how anybody could dislike them. True, on this farm (and many others) they eat a lot of grass and they soil lots more, but a flock of swans in flight is such a glorious sight. With their almost virginal white plumage and graceful slow-flapping and vast outstretched wings, they could pass for a low-flying

Fox catches rabbit in Wild Place.

Eamon McGarry trims a bull's hoof.

Eamon McGarry with Limousin stock bull, 'Clicker'.

Members of Laois Hunt lead a charity ride through Briggs'.

A flock of ducks fly over the Wild Place.

Spreading slurry on grassland.

Robin with William Goodwin of EV Condells.

A Whimbrel.

Robin is interviewed by Justin McCarthy, now Editor of the Irish Farmer's Journal.

February

Possibly triggered by the extremely mild weather, our farm experiences its first ever outbreak of infectious bovine rhinotracheitis (IBR) this month. Unfortunately, one beef bull does not respond to veterinary treatment and dies within 24 hours.

Apart from the IBR outbreak, this February is an uneventful month – the principal activity being the spreading of slurry on some silage ground. We recently changed our policy on when to spread fertiliser. Rather than use the calendar to help us determine when to do this, for the past couple of years we have been using a soil thermometer (which cost about €20) to confirm when soil temperatures have reached the desired 6-7°C.

February is also the month when the hoof trimmer, Eamon McGarry, gives our stock bulls the once-over at the end of the breeding season. If the bulls have injuries, bruises or other problems that need tending to, now is the time to carry out such tasks.

One stock bull has a bruise on his foot and the treatment for this involves trimming and cleaning the infected area before applying a glue-on shoe to allow the infected area to heal. These shoes are very handy because they do not need to be removed; they fall off themselves in time. The only other job that needs to be done is to trim another bull's hoof that has grown a long toe which, if left untended, will become very sore and make him lame.

Look past the colour

At first glance, there's nothing special about the cattle we breed. In fact, they look like a bunch of mongrels because they come in such a range of colours. This is in contrast to a herd where, say, the terminal sire (i.e. daddy) is a Charolais – in which case the offspring will usually be some shade of cream. Such colour uniformity conveys an image of order and status.

Most of our cows are Limousin, their colouring solid black or red with the occasional splash of white on the head. We use two breeds

of bull – Limousin and Belgian Blue – the latter being the reason for the calves' colour melange.

We use Limousin bulls on heifers; the offspring of this particular cross are usually red. Belgian Blues, on the other hand, have what is called coat colour polymorphism. As a result, they range from all-white to all-black and infinite shades of blue, including a characteristic blue roan; on top of that is the possibility of colour spotting. So, progeny colour is totally unpredictable. A few years ago, one of our red cows produced a snow-white calf. The following year, she produced a jet-black one. Both calves were by the same bull.

Fortunately, in this business colour is not

important. Shape (i.e. muscle) is what matters, and that is a feature which is consistently inherited, with the offspring's shape generally being, as far as can be determined, mid-way between the bull and the cow.

If the manufacturers of Carlsberg were in the beef breeding business, calves by a Belgian Blue bull out of a Limousin cow is what those folks would come up with. It's the ideal genetic combination as far as we are concerned.

Belgian Blues have a natural gene mutation known as double-muscling – a trait that was first documented in 1807. However, the breed wasn't developed commercially until the 1950s when a number of animals manifesting this particular trait were actively selected for breeding. Belgian Blues are the ultimate muscle-men... and women.

Of course they don't actually have two layers of muscling; rather, they have an increased number of muscle fibres which are particularly prevalent on their shoulders, back, loin and rib cage. These muscle fibres are associated with an increased ability to convert feed into lean muscle. The meat has a lower fat content,

making it highly desirable to the modern health-conscious consumer.

Belgian Blues are relatively fine-boned and this is one of the reasons why breeding bulls may develop lameness problems as they age. However, fears that their double-muscling trait would result in a disproportionate number of caesarean sections on this farm have thankfully proved unfounded. In fact, while we generally have as few as three or four caesareans a year, in 2012 we had just one. This is because the calves are not born with extreme muscling; it only begins to develop when they are aged between four and six weeks.

Another key trait of Belgian Blues is that they are docile – highly desirable from a herd management point of view. Limousins, in contrast, possess a certain proclivity for what is tactfully termed "negative docility". Despite Robin's persistent concerns about this rather undesirable trait, he has, after trying out a number of other breeds of cow, always reverted to Limousin. This is because they make the best mothers. They have a good ability to calve unassisted, they bond quickly

with their calves and they produce enough milk to rear them well.

The office

When asked what they dislike about their occupation, some farmers will list things like the interminable physicality, the wind, or always having to wear wellies. Most, however, will say that what they really, *really* detest is the paperwork – particularly the mandatory stuff required by the State which acts on behalf of the EU in the implementation of the CAP.

Part of the problem is that those who write the rules and prepare the forms are far removed – both psychologically and geographically – from the situation on the ground. What might seem straightforward and logical to officialdom can come across as mindboggling and impracticable to the farmer, for whom it is just a small (albeit usually critical) part of their working life.

Another aspect of the problem is that most farmers face into paperwork at the wrong time, i.e. at night when it is too late to do "proper" farm work. By this time, they do not have the

Recording calf identification details at tagging time.

Ann catches up on some paperwork.

requisite freshness of mind for the task. Moreover, if the paperwork process raises an issue that requires talking to an expert and getting their advice, the chances are that this person will not be contactable outside working hours. For this reason, the task will have to be shelved and the paperwork resumed at a later date – which is a good recipe for frustration and an even better recipe for errors.

A related version of this process is the 'shoebox syndrome' (shove it in a box until you have absolutely no choice but to deal with it). Robin is the exception to the rule: a self-confessed record nerd who has always operated on the principle of "when it happens, write it up". As I am the person who deals with a lot of the mandatory paperwork, it is lucky that Robin and I are on the same wavelength in terms of dealing with stuff as quickly as possible.

"I have always embraced record-keeping," says Robin. "Going back to the time when I had ewes, I always maintained accurate records. So, when record-keeping was made compulsory it was only an additional thread to what I was already doing."

Robin bought his first computer around 1990. Shortly afterwards, he began experimenting with spreadsheets; later he acquired one of the Kingswood programmes, and he then added others as they became available. "Honestly, I don't find the paperwork particularly onerous. But what really does annoy me is that for some reason we aren't trusted to run our businesses without documenting every little detail."

Outside of the regulatory requirements, Robin regards data availability as a key management tool, especially because of the large numbers of stock on our farm. Central to this is the Herd Register, which contains detailed dossiers on each animal – its health, its movements and its performance – in a level of detail that would be the envy of Interpol.

Over the years, we have had numerous inspections to check that we are operating as required. These have included a full-herd evaluation and a veterinary inspection by the Department of Agriculture, Food and the Marine as well as regular inspections by Bord Bia to verify our compliance with its Quality Assurance Scheme. "I was given a penalty on just one occasion," says Robin. "It was during the period when the percentage of set-aside

Robin in the jeep branch of the office.

was changing year to year. I used the wrong calculation, so it came up a bit short."

While we use the laptop for storing virtually all data, the information is recorded in the first instance using the old reliable (rainproof) *peann luaidhe*. Several clipboards containing records of recent events are to be found lying on the dashboard or passenger seat of the jeep – close at hand if information needs to be verified. The records are key to day-to-day management of the farm. For example, if a calf is sick and needs to be brought in from the field for treatment, its mother can be quickly identified based on the information contained in these clipboard files.

Every February, Robin pulls out a couple of sheets of ruled A4 paper, writes 'Scanning' across the top of each sheet and then creates a series of columns titled 'Cow number', 'Days' (in calf) and 'Tags' (noting how many each cow has, just in case any tags have been lost and need to be re-ordered). Towards the end of July, he repeats the process, creating 'Calf registration' sheets comprising columns titled 'Calf number', 'Check Digit' (part of the animal's unique identification)', 'Calf sex', 'Cow number' and, finally, one titled 'Comments' (which covers issues relating to calving such as whether it involved farmer or veterinary assistance).

Legally, all calves must be tagged with the prescribed 12-digit ear tag before they are twenty days old and their births registered within the following seven days. We have a practice of tagging our calves within a couple of days of birth and subsequently registering

Robin records the weight of a bull.

them online. Because we have the option of carrying out online registration at any hour of the day or night, we no longer have to race into the village in order to catch the evening post. In this respect, the electronic age has proved a godsend.

In the case of our stock bulls – of which we have six — there are several reasons for recording which bull covers which cow. The attribution of the correct sire details on the breeding record in turn feeds into the performance record of the bull in question and helps future decision-making on how he is used (or not!). It also helps us establish what breed of calf is expected to be delivered. Finally, and critically, it helps to pinpoint any fertility problems.

During 2012 when we were scanning our cows, the pregnancies in one particular group seemed to be approximately 40 days behind the others. This indicated a problem with one of the bulls. The ensuing process of checking our computer records identified one bull which

was then earmarked for fertility tests.

Our management records contain the results of beef cattle weighed at specific intervals (to monitor their weight gain). Statutory records cover issues such as spraying (the date, the rate of application, the product name and the serial number), as well as the consumption of concentrate feed and the usage of fertiliser.

We also use the laptop to make our online VAT returns and to complete the Teagasc Profit Monitor. In our eyes, the usefulness of the Profit Monitor lies not so much in comparing our farm's performance with other farms, rather in comparing our farm's performance in any given year to its performance in each previous year. In other words, while it doesn't indicate whether or not we are doing better or worse than other farms, it highlights relevant trends in relation to our own farm. As such, we can use it to identify whether individual changes we have made produced positive or negative outcomes.

Computers are undoubtedly a useful tool but at times it's the operators that fall down on the job! While I think I am pretty accurate in terms of inputting information, there would be the occasional typo; like the time I was entering information on the sale of a heifer and in the box for "price/kg" instead inserted the "(total) price" and obviously didn't cast a quick eye back over the information before hitting "Save". The net result is that the heifer showed up as making the guts of half a million euro! Robin was the one who later copped the mistake and commented that "we could do with a few more of them". What a wit!

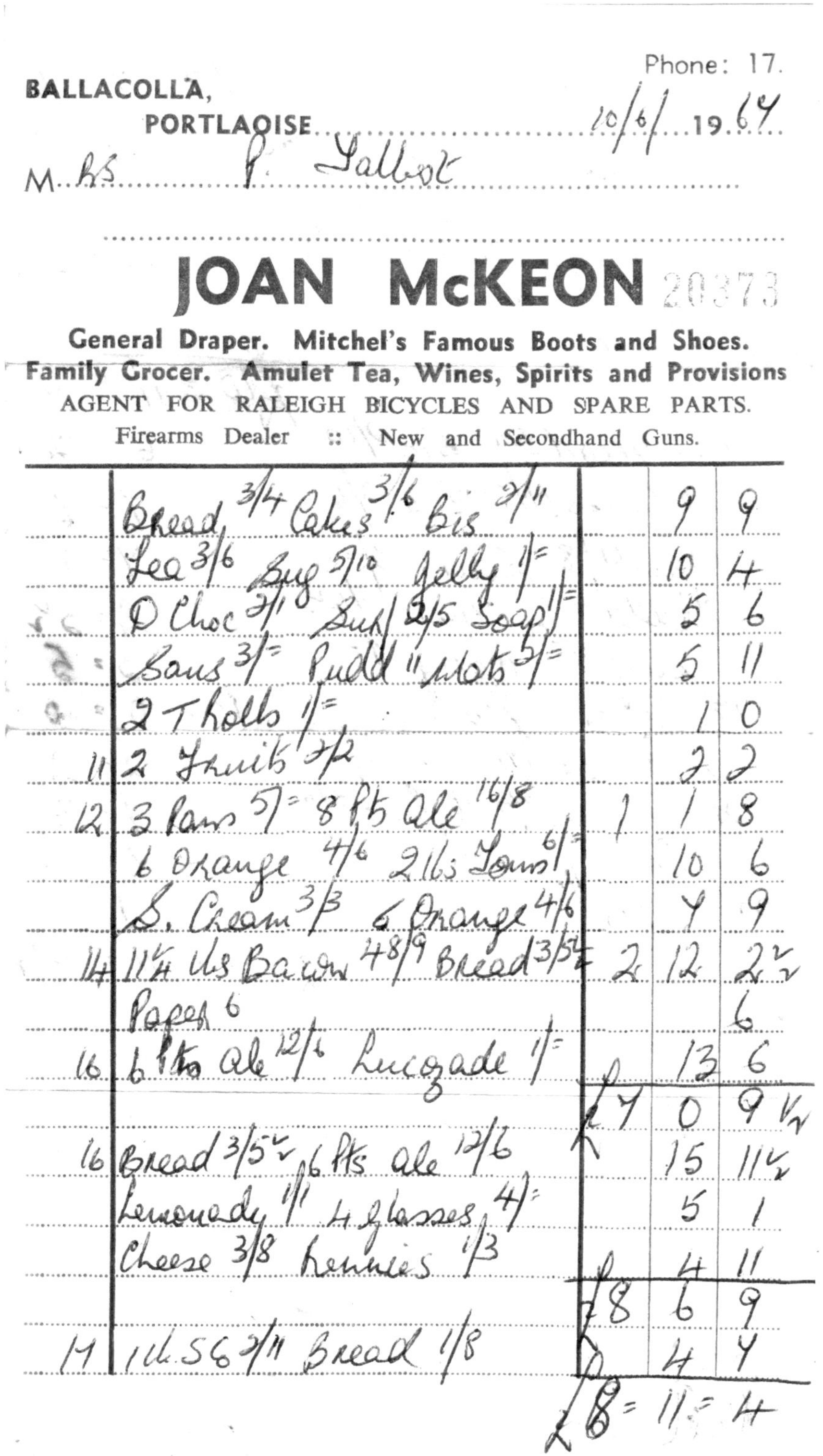

BALLACOLLA,
PORTLAOISE.

Phone: 17.

10/6/ 19.67.

M.rs P. Talbot

JOAN McKEON 20373

General Draper. Mitchel's Famous Boots and Shoes.
Family Grocer. Amulet Tea, Wines, Spirits and Provisions
AGENT FOR RALEIGH BICYCLES AND SPARE PARTS.
Firearms Dealer :: New and Secondhand Guns.

Bread 3/4 Cakes 3/6 Bis 2/11		9	9
Tea 3/6 Sug 5/10 Jelly 1/=		10	4
D Choc 3/1 Suet 2/5 Soap 1/=		5	6
Sans 3/= Pudd 1/1 Mats 5/=		5	11
2 Tholls 1/=		1	0
11. 2 Fruits 2/2		2	2
12. 3 Pans 5/= 8 Pts Ale 16/8	1	1	8
6 Orange 4/6 2 lbs Tom 6/=		10	6
S. Cream 3/3 6 Orange 4/6		4	9
14 11¼ lbs Bacon 48/9 Bread 3/5½	2	12	2½
Paper 6			6
16 6 Pts Ale 12/6 Lucozade 1/=		13	6
	£7	0	9½
16 Bread 3/5½ 6 Pts Ale 12/6		15	11½
Lemonade 1/1 4 glasses 4/=		5	1
Cheese 3/8 Pennies 1/3		4	11
	£8	6	9
17 1 lb S6 2/11 Bread 1/8		4	4
	£8 =	11 =	4

(Left): Grocery bill from 1967. Very different from today.

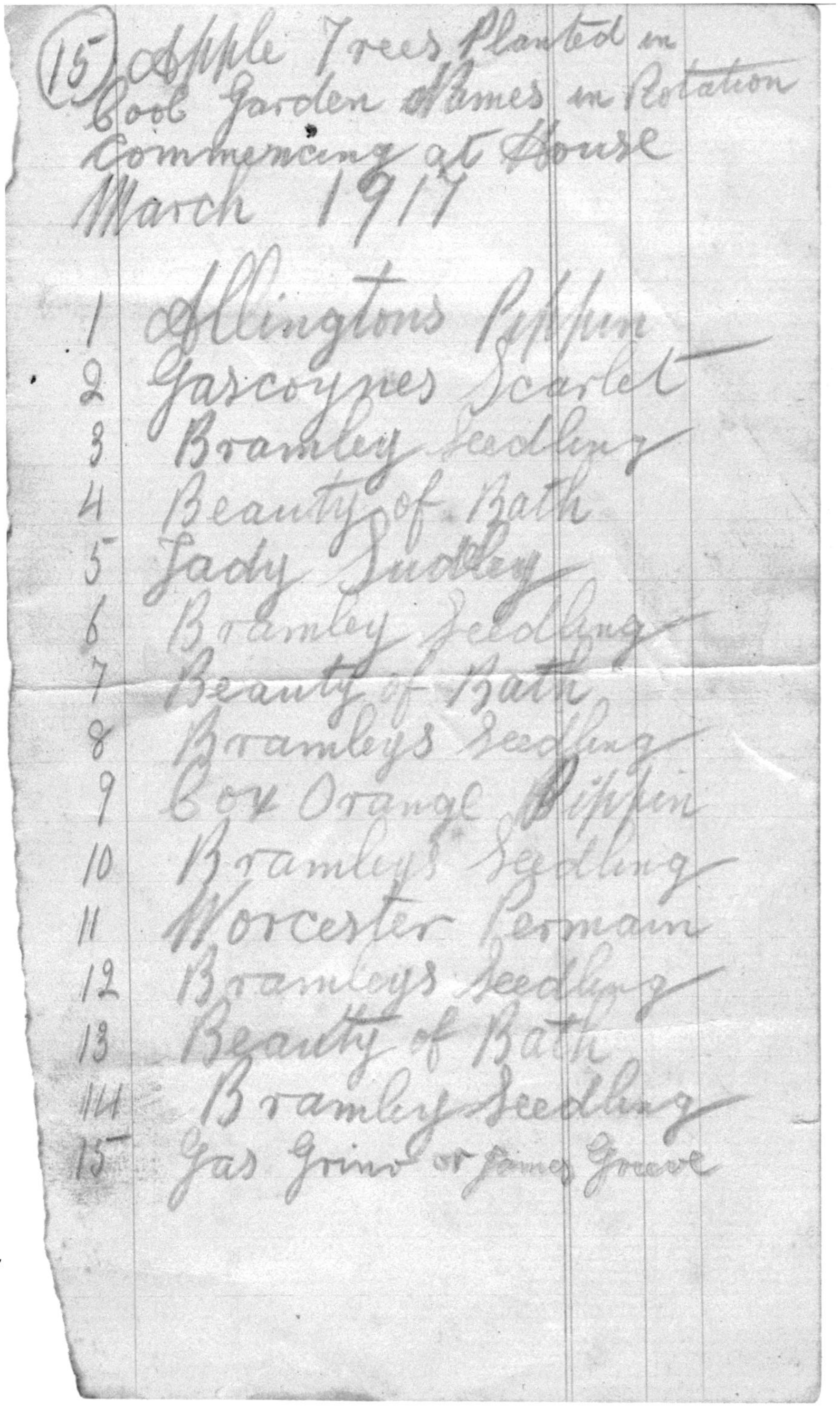

15. Apple Trees Planted in
Cool Garden Names in Rotation
Commencing at House
March 1917

1	Allingtons Pippin
2	Gascoynes Scarlet
3	Bramley Seedling
4	Beauty of Bath
5	Lady Sudley
6	Bramley Seedling
7	Beauty of Bath
8	Bramleys Seedling
9	Cox Orange Pippin
10	Bramleys Seedling
11	Worcester Permain
12	Bramleys Seedling
13	Beauty of Bath
14	Bramley Seedling
15	Gas Grind or James Grieve

(Right): A list of apple trees planted in 1917.

Headstone in the old Killermogh graveyard with church ruins on the right.

KILERMO CHURCH, BALLACOLLA.

Killermogh church pictured around 1905.

Killermogh church today.

Sunlight streams through the spaced roof onto beef bull.

Frank Yorke and Kurt Krous, both from Errill, take a break from cutting the grass for the Tidy Towns.

Robin and Sarah.

Sunrise over the Wild Place.

Sarah and Ruth.

This March continues a period of very dry weather lasting several weeks. For the first time that Robin can recall, all the cattle we put out to pasture are grazing on lush grass for a full week before St Patrick's Day.

The long, dry, bright spell enables a lot of work to be done on the tillage ground, and our daughters Sarah and Ruth have a ball picking stones off the field to prevent damage to the sower and later the combine.

The two big jobs that must be completed before releasing our stock from the sheds to the fields are TB testing and scanning the cows for pregnancy. Scanning is always an anxious time but on this occasion we are happy with the results, which show only 6-7 % of them empty. In one group, the pregnancies are approximately 40 days behind the others.

The hassle of the TB test

"The annual TB test – it's the one week of the

Bawling cows.

year I truly hate," says Robin. "It's very stressful both physically and mentally for man and beast. Every animal has to be rounded up and put into the cattle crush on two occasions in a period of four days. You try to separate the calves from the cows before they go into the crush while simultaneously ensuring that the calves don't get walked on. Then there's the bawling – cows looking for their calves and vice versa, with the vet and ourselves stuck in the middle."

But the biggest issue for Robin is that this traumatising routine has been going on year after year all his farming life, and there's no end in sight.

Ireland's Bovine TB eradication programme was introduced in 1950. It has been so spectacularly unsuccessful that Robin believes it should now be accepted for what it is, a containment programme, which is what it will remain until the part played by the badger (*Meles meles*) is resolved – whether by testing, the use of a long-awaited vaccination or some other approach. Other countries have managed to eradicate TB but those that have done so do not have to

Armed for action, vet Ken Quinlan arrives.

Pat Whelan records the tag numbers.

contend with a wildlife species in which TB is endemic and which shares the same environment as cattle.

Robin strongly believes that the scheme should be fundamentally reformed in order to bring it into line with 21st century best practice. It should be made a lot more farmer-friendly and livestock-friendly, and he believes this could be achieved without weakening the effectiveness of the scheme.

Department figures show that cows account for almost two-thirds of reactors (64%) while calves make up just 2%. Robin has never heard of an incidence where the only reactor in a herd was a young calf and therefore he questions the necessity to test cattle aged under, say, six months. The rules allow the test to be completed over a period of two weeks, therefore it should be possible to test the older cattle first. "Of course, if a reactor were to be detected, then you would move in and test all the remaining animals ASAP," he says.

In herds where there has been no reactor in the previous five years, Robin suggests moving to bi-annual testing while retaining the pre-movement test. He also suggests that cattle within a few months of slaughter should not be tested as they will be subjected to a post-mortem test in the abattoir in any event.

Department figures show that 18,476 reactors were identified in 2012. While this figure is a long way from the 139,881 reactors recorded in 1961, reactor numbers have remained almost static since 2009.

In contrast to previous comments by Department officials that the endgame is in sight, when the most recent figures were released Minister Simon Coveney was quoted as saying he was hopeful that the incidence of TB could be maintained at or below present levels. In doing so he was perhaps unwittingly admitting that he accepts the disease is not going to be eradicated any time soon. If this is indeed the case, the drive for reform should get under way as soon as possible.

Macnas, the joy of freedom

In the wonderfully colourful and expressive Irish language, Macnas means joyful

abandonment; some farmers use the term to describe the madness of (particularly) the young cow when she is set free to the field in spring. Like any wild animals freed from a cage, our cows and calves are always ecstatic on such occasions. They are so excited they don't know quite what to do – graze or gallop, eat or exercise. They love both options. Blinded by the sunlight and drunk with excitement, they want to do it all at the same time in case their freedom is rescinded once again.

They're not really hungry, but this is grass after all. And not just any grass, it's the first grass of the year and truly the sweetest – a fact that means more to the cows than it does to the calves. The cows have been here before and they know what it's all about. As they regard all the open space in front of them as far as the eye can see, they just want to run and run. Having been cooped up for so long, they are finally free. Such joy!

This is the one occasion when the cows do not take a back seat in favour of their offspring. As soon as they realise they are going to be released into the field, they push their way to

the back of the trailer. While the majority leap off the ramp in unbounded ecstasy, there are always a few that will momentarily freeze before scanning their surroundings in wide-eyed disbelief and then take off at speed. Most of them are so caught up in their euphoria that they rarely check to see if their calves are following behind them. The calves might have the fresher limbs but this is one race that the cows always win. Not that they know why they are racing. Their legs seem to take on a life of their own. They want to run… and they might never stop.

But they don't just run. They also buck and leap, twist and turn, kick and spin, accompanied by the occasional uncontrollable fart, every inch and ounce of their bodies on high alert, pumping adrenalin driving them into high-level dressage moves that would be the envy of any half-decent Lipizzaner.

After one (usually), two (occasionally) or three (rarely) laps around the perimeter of the field, the cows finally run out of steam. This brings a wave of relief to their trailing calves which are pumping sweat and frothing at the

mouth. Whereas in the sheds, the calves were always the ones leading the way in the frolicking stakes, now it comes as a shock to them to realise that their mammies can still put on a performance and are not merely the ever-willing suppliers of high-octane hydration for their offspring.

As for the cows, they begin to take stock of their surroundings, look at themselves and each other in surprise, a little mystified though not the least embarrassed by their own behaviour. What in God's name were we doing running around the place like idiots when there is all this lovely lush grass just waiting to be eaten? Once this realisation begins to dawn on them, they lower their heads and don't raise them again until many hours later when their bellies are hurting – like children who have gorged themselves on too much chocolate on Easter Sunday.

The great release is equally welcomed by us farmers as it marks a sharp decrease (though not the end) of time expended on the daily feed/bed regime. Any cattle heading for slaughter in the coming few months must remain indoors as they are subjected to an intensive feeding regime which would be incompatible with the aforementioned physical exertions.

Within a couple of hours, the palpable excitement of the released cows wears off and is replaced by a mellowness that seems to permeate every cell of their bodies. By now, cows and calves alike have settled into their new environment, with most of the cows lying down chewing their cuds, the calves stretched out nearby soaking up the first rays of spring sunshine that they have ever experienced. Such bliss!

Interestingly, the cows' return indoors in eight months' time will be greeted with an almost equivalent level of palpable pleasure. Cattle have their own understanding of the seasons and when the ground gets cold and wet and the grass becomes scarce and soggy, they know that the time has come to enjoy once again the experience of having their food served up to them, followed by curling up in a nice fresh bed of straw.

Liam Dunne, *pregnancy scanning operator*

Liam Dunne provides a cow and ewe pregnancy diagnosis service for which he is always in great demand throughout most of the midlands, but mainly in Laois, Offaly, Tipperary, North Kilkenny and the neighbouring counties. Despite the logistics of the job, which some might find less than appealing, he loves what he does.

"Of course, you would get bad days," he says, "especially where there's a small flock of maybe twenty-five to thirty ewes and the ram hasn't been working. The farmer would often be dumbfounded. It can be very costly news and of course I would be disappointed on their behalf."

But, Liam adds, once the shock has worn off, the farmers always say it is better to know the truth. All along, they will have been feeding their ewes based on the assumption that they were pregnant. Then, suddenly, they have to come to terms with the fact that they are empty and the feeding regime has been a waste of time. As a result, the farmer now needs to make different plans.

Liam Dunne was reared on a drystock farm in nearby Aghaboe. In 1990, he became one of the first people in Ireland to offer a cow pregnancy scanning service. Prior to that, sheep pregnancy scanning was the only similar type of service on offer. But scanning sheep is a very different proposition to scanning cows (the former requires turning the sheep on their backs). Liam had only recently joined the Farm Relief Service when the previous pregnancy scanning operator retired. He was offered the opportunity to take the other operator's place on completion of the requisite training course in England.

He scans about 50 cows an hour and somewhere between 800 and 1,000 ewes a day on an average of three to four farms. The biggest flock that he visits, in Tipperary, tops 2,800 ewes. Each year he scans somewhere in the region of 40,000 ewes, including around 10,000 in the Comeragh Mountains. "I love going down there (the Comeraghs)," says Liam. "It's a very different scene; people are just so laid back and they have a great outlook on life."

While the scanning of ewes tends to be restricted to the period December to February, in the case of both sucklers and dairy cows it may be carried out during any month of the year. Liam says the biggest change he has seen in his business over the past five years is that the average size of dairy herds has almost doubled.

The scanner he uses is an Oviscan 4, which he admits is not the latest technology but it is the technology that he is most comfortable with. "Some experts use ultrasound goggles but I prefer to look at the image on the screen."

Although he works on his own he does not find his job at all lonely. Everywhere he goes there are people waiting for him, most of them more than happy to have a chat. "I love the life, going from farm to farm, never being stuck too long in one place. It's not at all solitary," says Liam, who is a GAA stalwart in his downtime.

He doesn't have a preference between cows or sheep but he does admit that sheep are cleaner (to scan). He also points out that working with cows is very physical, that his scanning arm can get tired after a long day. "It could catch up with you when you are 50," he says, before adding with a laugh, "so I have another ten years!"

A heavily pregnant cow at sunset.

Three wise men, Robin, Liam Dunne and Joe Hyland.

Liam washes up after scanning.

Liam reads the screen as he scans a cow.

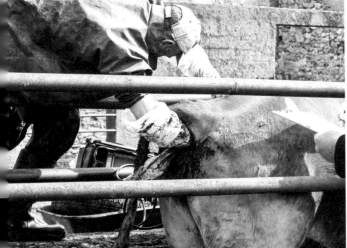

Liam Dunne.

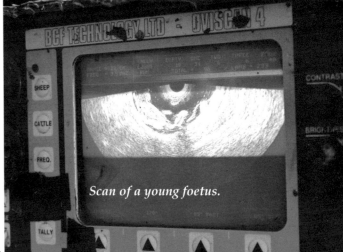

Scan of a young foetus.

Gerry Giggins, *animal nutritionist*

Looking for the best impartial advice on ruminant nutrition, or want to know what's really going on at the coalface of Irish agriculture? Well, there's only one person to call: Gerry Giggins from Ardee, Co Louth.

Generations of Gerry's family worked on the land locally and, from a very young age, he was spending a lot of time with neighbour Maxwell McKeever, who Gerry describes as "a huge influence – a great exponent of modern farming techniques and one of the most progressive farmers of his generation."

Gerry studied at Ballyhaise Agricultural College and in his final year he travelled as an exchange student to a Dutch college which was home to an 800-head bull beef farm. On his return to Ireland in 1979, Gerry's plan was to take up a job with Maxwell McKeever. Sadly, Maxwell died in an accident and Gerry subsequently joined Bord na Móna, which at that time was in the process of establishing a bull beef enterprise. Later, he took up a similar position with Larry Goodman in AIBP.

In 1996, he joined feeder wagon manufacturer Richard Keenan & Co as beef development manager and, two years later, he helped to set up the KK beef club, a new type of partnership linking nutritional advice to farmer and processor – an enterprise that has helped to promote Ireland's beef export trade with Italy.

Today, Gerry continues his relationship with Keenan as a consultant on the development of his nutritional advice provision concept for worldwide application. He has also set up his own company, Nutrition Link, working with around 200 cattle and sheep farmers across Ireland.

Other than his affiliation with Keenan, he has consciously avoided aligning himself with any of the vested interests in agriculture. This has proved an advantage for Irish farmers as they can be sure that the information he gives is balanced and impartial.

He is in regular contact with people from the across the agricultural industry, from the bottom to the top, talking to them on the phone as well as at meetings, trade shows and other events. "I don't wait for information to come to me, I go chase it. On a daily basis I glean as much information from my clients as I impart to them."

Robin keeps in regular contact with Gerry, especially heading into the winter months. During Gerry's visit here every October, Robin outlines his plans for various groups of cattle and Gerry sketches out a diet for each (suckling cows, creep feed for their calves and fattening bulls/heifers) based on the farm's silage results, the volumes of home-grown barley available and the current market price of additional ingredients. He does this in a way that is designed to minimise costs and maximise margins.

Within hours of receiving Gerry's email containing the final version of the recommended diets, Robin writes them out on a card and sticks them up on the tractor dashboard for daily reference. Implicit in all of this is the principle of healthy feeding. These diets are reviewed regularly, taking into account animal performance, stocks of various feed held on the farm and any major fluctuation in the cost of bought-in ingredients.

"I have a strong compassion for animals and I firmly believe in the principle of healthy eating. A healthy rumen means a happy animal which, in turn, means better performance, better quality meat and more profit," says Gerry. However, he fears that Ireland is being outpaced in terms of feed technology.

"We can produce plenty of good grass, which is great, but it's not enough." While a lot of work on genetics is being carried out in Ireland, he is disappointed at the lack of research in matching this work to advances in the area of feed technology. This is in sharp contrast to work that is happening in other countries.

Given Gerry's vast knowledge of Irish agriculture, coupled with his sharp wit and gregarious personality, it was almost inevitable that he would put these talents to further use at some point. And indeed he has; his latest venture being Farm Tours Ireland which he is running with son Aonghus. "I am passionate about showcasing Ireland, bringing people to see everything from commercial beef production to producing artisan foods."

In his downtime, in addition to being an ardent Leinster rugby supporter Gerry busies himself with his quarter-acre organic garden.

Through his work with Richard Keenan &

Robin with Gerry Giggins and son Aonghus.

Gerry Giggins.

Visitors from the Czech Republic.

Robin and Gerry discuss cattle diets.

Alain Boulainger, Keenan sales manager in Quebec, Canada, Rana Hussain, Keenan sales manager in Pakistan, Iran and Saudi Arabia with Gerry Giggins and Robin.

Co, he has visited almost 30 countries around the world and in the process he has had many adventures and a few close scrapes, including being mugged, escaping a near-hijacking and having his passport seized in the Middle East. And then there was the time he travelled to Argentina a couple of days after he had been bitten by a dog in Ireland. Between the language barrier and Argentina's experience with rabies, he almost ended up having his leg amputated.

It's a full life.

Spreading straw.

Cow with ten month old bull calf.

Garry Roe, *contractor*

Gary Roe is lucky. Not just because he has built a new house, has recently got married (to Cathy-Ann Menton), works at a job he enjoys in an environment he loves, is blessed with a good social life and a close family, and has achieved all of this at the relatively young age of 29. What sets Gary apart is that he recognises and appreciates his good luck.

Gary and his father, Clifford, run a farm together and also run a contracting business. "It's Clifford's business but I am mostly the one who is on the road," says Gary, who is among the first of his father's peers' sons to farm.

Combining contracting with farming is what Gary has always wanted to do. As a child, he and his cousin David (Roe) used to climb tractors and play games along the lines of "Right, who will we go to today? I'm ploughing, you can sow." While he had originally intended to go to university after finishing school he ended up taking a year out to go to Gurteen Agricultural College. He then headed to Australia and enjoyed a year or so there before returning to work on the farm in Tinraheen.

Gary and Clifford sold their sheep a few years ago because the "land was tired of them". While Gary misses the livestock, he doesn't miss the arguments. On the subject of working with his father, he says: "Yes, we do have arguments … same as any father and son, especially when you have two strong opinions… but not as many as we used to have."

The Roes are primarily tillage contractors but they also do other work including dung and slurry spreading. These latter jobs can be somewhat odorous and, when I ask if they have ever impacted on his social life, Gary smiles and says: "A good shower works wonders," pointing out that handling wrapped silage bales can be far worse… "You know to wear gloves if you're planning a night out."

They rent a lot of tillage land and do a fair bit of their own sowing in the winter as it spreads the workload and justifies having good machinery. But everything has to pay its way. "Profit in contracting is a curious thing. You could work for three days solid, then get a breakdown and the profits you have made simply disappear."

Gary loves watching the progress of crops they have sown, and he gets a buzz coming up to the harvest. "You could be doing eighty- to one hundred-hour weeks for a month or more. While that's not a problem… I'm always glad when it's over." He struggles to give me a list of his dislikes of the job and finally comes up with "the pressure to please when you are trying to get to everyone at once, especially during broken weather."

Gary is upbeat about the future. "You'll never become a millionaire as a result of working the land… but there's more to life. A lot of people my age are still trying to find their feet. I know where I want to be in ten years' time." Which is? "Maybe with a bit more machinery, but basically still doing what I'm doing. Hopefully."

Clifford and Gary Roe pictured in Kilkenny on the latter's wedding day in October.

Gary spreads FYM or dung on the stubbles on Simon's Hill.

Gary Roe.

Gary cleans out a cattle shed.

Recipes

Our breakfast:

Nutty Spiced Granola

Ingredients
6 cups Flahavan's Organic Porridge oats
1 cup chopped nuts of choice
1 cup sunflower seeds
1 teaspoon grated nutmeg
1 tablespoon ground cinnamon
1 cup raisins or sultanas
½ cup sunflower oil
¾ cup maple syrup (I generally try to use Irish-products whenever possible but personally, I prefer maple syrup to honey.)

Method
Pre-heat oven to 150°C.
Place all the dry ingredients except the fruit in a large bowl and combine well.
Add the oil and the maple syrup. Toss again, mixing thoroughly.
Empty into large roasting tin. (I have tried cutting out the first step and just pouring everything into the roasting tin before mixing but I found that rather than coating the drying ingredients the liquid is inclined to run straight to the bottom and stick).
Place in oven and turn every 10 minutes until evenly browned.
Store for up to six weeks in an airtight container.

Their breakfast:

High-performance body-builder (finisher) diet

Feeder loading order, fresh weight, kg/head
1.2kg wheaten straw
3kg maize meal
1.8kg cane molasses
0.25kg soyabean meal
2.5kg rolled barley
0.06kg beef mineral
5.8kg beef intensive ration
2 kg grass silage

Method
Calculate the total weight of each ingredient required, based on the number of animals to be fed.
Park the feeder wagon in a convenient location, engage the power take off (PTO) shaft and increase the revs on the tractor to 1,500.
Climb aboard the loader and, using the bucket attached on front, load all the ingredients, except the silage, in designated order, carefully adding the correct amount of each ingredient using the weigh cell on the feeder wagon.
While the ingredients are mixing, detach the bucket from the loader, pick up the shear grab and add the correct amount of silage.
Park the loader, proceed to the tractor and begin feeding immediately.
Repeat daily.

Talbot family history

Forte et fidele: Strong and faithful.

Talbot is a long established and distinguished family name dating back hundreds of years in Europe. Its etymology is disputed. While generally regarded as Anglo-Norman there is a suggestion that it may have German roots, Talebod, which means "bright valley" while derivatives from French include "messenger of destruction", "to cut fagots" (bundles of sticks for firewood), while Talebot means lampblack in Normandy and it is an old local nickname for bandits who blackened their faces to avoid recognition.

What is known is that Talbots were with William the Conqueror when he invaded England in 1066 and Richard Talbot is mentioned in the Domesday Book of 1086. A descendent of his, also called Richard, came to Ireland in 1170 and Talbots are now to be found all over the world.

The Talbot name has had a long connection with religious life, several members of the family being bishops in Ireland while Richard Talbot, a younger brother of the first Earl of Shrewsbury, became Archbishop of Dublin as well as Lord Chancellor of Ireland and was one of the most influential Irish statesmen of the time.

While much of the family, including this branch, is Protestant, other religions, particularly Catholicism, are also represented: for example, the Venerable Matt Talbot (1856-1925), a reformed drunk who became devoutly religious. A number of the Earls of Shrewsbury were Catholic and one was even a priest.

The Earl of Shrewsbury was recreated in 1442 when the celebrated warrior, more brave soldier than general, John Talbot was made the first Earl. Described by Shakespeare as "The Scourge of the French" and in political rhymes of the time as "our goode dogge", though it is unclear whether this is a reference to his loyalty or a play on his name (a talbot also being a large, heavy, mostly white hound of the time with pendulous ears and drooping jowls; believed to be the ancestor of the modern bloodhound it is now extinct, apparently because of its lack of purpose and need for constant care).

Incidentally, this John Talbot once proposed a law that Englishmen should not wear moustaches lest they would be taken for Irishmen. He has enjoyed a more recent incarnation under the name Talbot as one of the primary protagonists in the Sony PSP game Jeanne d'Arc.

Talbot has also become a personal name, the name of several ships, a number of towns including the Welsh coastal Port Talbot, a mining town in Victoria, Australia, while it is also the name of a dessert service, a good Bordeaux called Château Talbot, as well as being a common name for hotels and pubs. There is also a trait known as The Talbot Finger, a fusion of two bones of the fingers, more correctly known as symphalangism. (And, no, Robin doesn't have it!)

Monnamonra, Clonburren, Coole

When I started looking at the family tree, Pam handed me a note written by one of the relations which apparently showed this branch of the family as being directly descended from one of the Earls of Shrewsbury. "Great," I thought, "job done." However, on closer inspection it proved to be wrong. There are also various anecdotal family links to the Talbots of Malahide but again I could not verify them. What can be said is that in the middle of the 19th century "our" Talbots were tenant farmers near Rathdowney, Co Laois. The earliest currently verifiable record of the family's presence in the area is contained in a letter dated 1821. The letter cites a Benjamin Talbot of Monnamonra as one of four men recommended for the new peace preservation force, and describes the men as "loyal Good Protestants."

In order to ascertain the likely status of the family at this time and to place their status in a broader context, I contacted local historian Dr Jack Carter. The first question he asked was "Were they Catholic or Protestant?"

In those days, religion was a significant factor in Ireland, especially though not exclusively when it came to State employment. "To be a Protestant ensured a certain status and protection, the perception being that you were loyalist, reliable, honest and hardworking, with a reverse implicit presumption that you were none of those things unless you were Protestant," Jack explains.

Griffith's Valuation (1851-52) records a Benjamin Talbot as renting 48 acres in Monnamonra from the Stubber Estate as well as a further 38 acres and a house in nearby Heath/Castlefleming – which would have been considered a sizeable holding at the time.

It is likely that Benjamin Talbot lived in Heath House, which was later destroyed by fire.

The Rathdowney Church of Ireland Register records the birth of a son, Benjamin, to a Peter and Catherine Talbot on 10 November 1792. While there were other Talbots in the area, the timeframe, coupled with the subsequent continued use of the names Peter, Catherine and Benjamin in the family, would indicate that this is "our" Benjamin. Benjamin married Elizabeth Pearson in 1826 and they had seven sons (the three youngest of whom became farmers) and two daughters. William (born 1827) emigrated to Australia; Peter (1828); John, emigrated to America; Henry was killed in the Crimean War; Elizabeth (born 1834) married local farmer William Watson; Catherine married James Morris of Abbeyleix; Benjamin (born 1836) married Jane Wellwood of Clonking, Abbeyleix; Robert (born 1839) married Aphra Pratt and lived in Clonburren, and Joseph (Joe) (1844), who was manager of the brewery in Rathdowney, married Emily Garrett. They lived in the Heath before moving first to Birr and then to Canada. Within a generation, the family had scattered far and wide.

Clonburren is just a few kilometres from the Heath as the crow flies. The first reference I found in relation to the Talbot family in Clonburren was on Benjamin's death certificate which records his death as having occurred there in 1864 at the residence of his son, Benjamin.

At some point before 1870, Robert took over the house at Clonburren and Benjamin and Jane became the first Talbots to move to Coole. They had five sons and two daughters:

Benjamin (born 1870), Frances (1871), Joseph (1873), Peter (1874), Elizabeth (1876), John (1878-1880) and Robert (1880). Benjamin (Senior) died in August the following year from typhoid at the age of 45. Throughout the early part of the 19th century there had been major epidemics of this disease in Ireland, particularly during the Famine, but sporadic outbreaks continued for some time after that.

Benjamin's death may not have been the only difficulty in the extended family at the time. Jack Carter, in his book *The Land Wars and its Leaders in Queen's County 1879-82*, refers to an 1881 letter in which a Robert Talbot had paid £44.18s.2d for a half year's rent to Lord Castletown via a merchant in Rathdowney, as he didn't dare to be seen paying it directly to the landlord's agent. This is most likely a reference to "our" Robert, in Clonburren.

This action would not have been popular at the height of the Land Wars, but every one of us has some ancestors who made decisions primarily for reasons of self-preservation; if they hadn't, we would probably not be here today. According to Jack Carter, paying rents in secret was far from uncommon – and not just among Protestants – because the fear of eviction for failing to do so was very real. Indeed, he points to the well-known story of a priest elsewhere in the county who was a leading activist during the Land Wars but was actually paying his own rent on the quiet.

Benjamin and Jane, Robin's great-grandparents, took on the rental of 170 acres in Coole. This land was subsequently bought out by their son Peter in 1913, for £300.

When Robin's mum, Pam, arrived here on her marriage to Bob in 1951, she had the job of feeding the men who worked here. "Dinner was always at twelve o'clock when the Angelus bell rang in Ballacolla. No matter who came to the door at meal time, they were fed," she says.

"The threshing was the biggest job, and one year we had 26 helpers. As well as making dinner for all of them, we brought out tea and jam sandwiches to the haggard at four o'clock. Later, in the evening, some of the men would come in to the house for tea. We also gave them beer, which we kept inside the back door and brought out in a bucket two or three times a day."

Bob was hardworking and ambitious and, having made the best of the disastrous 1941 outbreak of FMD, he subsequently operated two threshing machines in the locality for many years, paving the way for the expansion of the farm in the 1950s. One of these land purchases was a wedding anniversary present for Pam; generous on the one hand, astute on the other.

Unfortunately, a poor recovery from an appendix operation, coupled with an unwillingness to rest and a penchant for fatty meat, contributed to Bob's untimely death in 1963 at the age of 47. Pam then ran the farm until Robin joined her after sitting his Inter Cert in 1972. Together, they purchased additional land and also undertook some consolidation of the business.

Since Robin and I got married, our focus has been on continuing to improve the farm infrastructure, in accordance with statutory requirements, and on trying to build a solid base to enable us to successfully face whatever challenges lie ahead.

Peter and Harriet (nee Melbourne) Talbot, Robin's grandparents.

Robin and Ann on their wedding day.

Superintendent Registrar's District *Donaghmore*					Registrar's District *Rathdowney*			
18 64.	DEATHS Registered in the District of *Rathdowney* in the Union of *Donaghmore* in the Count of *Queens*							
No.	Date and Place of Death	Name and Surname	Sex.	Condition.	Age last Birthday.	Rank, Profession, or Occupation.	Certified Cause of Death, and Duration of Illness.	Signature, Qualification, and Residence of Informant.	When Registered.	Signature of Registrar.
7	Jan 21 1864 Clonbyrne	Ben Talbot	Male	Married	77 years	Farmer	Strangulated Hernia Three days ill	Benjamin Talbot present Farmer Clonbyrne	Feb 4 1864	Henry Smith

1864 death certificate of Ben Talbot, Robin's great-great grandfather.

Bob and Pamela Jackson, on their wedding day in 1951.

TO THE REGISTRAR OF DEEDS IN IRELAND.

A **Memorial** of an Indenture made the   day of   One Thousand Nine Hundred and *Thirteen* Between *Peter Talbot* of *Cool* the County of *Queens* County Tenant Farmer thereinafter called the Tenant of the one part and THE COMMISSIONERS PUBLIC WORKS IN IRELAND acting in execution of the Land Law (Ireland) Act, 1881, and of the Landed Property Improvement (Ireland) cts as defined by the said Land Law (Ireland) Act 1881 thereinafter called the Commissioners of the other part whereby after reciting at the Tenant *was* occupier of the lands specified in the First Schedule thereto (which are also specified in the Schedule hereunder ritten), thereinafter called the Holding, and as therein IT WAS WITNESSED that the Tenant in pursuance of the agreement therein entioned, and in consideration of *Three Hundred* Pounds to be lent as therein mentioned, d thereby charge the Holding and all *his* tenancy, estate and interest therein, with the payment to the Commissioners of all advances ade in pursuance of the said agreement, with interest on such advances at the rate therein mentioned, which said Indenture as to the ecution thereof by the Tenant is witnessed by

THE SCHEDULE REFERRED TO

hat Part of the Townland of *Cool* situate in the Barony of *Clarmallag* d County of *Queens* County containing *161* Acres *and 10 perches* Statute easure or thereabouts.

Signed and Sealed by the Tenant in presence of

Jane Talbot?

Clonburren.

Talbot visitors from South Africa: Greg Talbot, his wife Ronell, his sister Wendy, Pam, Wendy's husband Keith Kelly and Robin.

Dr Alan Kelly, UCD, Dr Karina Pierce, UCD and Pres ASA, Robin and agri-journalist, John Shirley.

Pat Halley selects stock for the beef factory.

Ruth – How do I comb that mane?

Feeding silage when the cherry blosssom is in bloom.

A row of tractors at the Laois Down Syndrome fundraiser.

Top dressing spring barley with nitrogen.

A row of cows look (at me) over the hedge.

April

In terms of weather, this is the most topsy-turvy month of the year, and 2012 generally is a topsy-turvy year.

During the first few weeks we manage to get the spring barley sown in ideal conditions. What a joy to live in Ireland when the weather is good; people working on the land in their t-shirts with the sun on their backs. Barley explodes into life.

Suddenly, however, the weather turns. It gets very cold and starts to rain. In order to give the grass a chance to grow, we revert to feeding the cows and calves with silage.

April is also marked by a visit from members of the Agricultural Science Association.

Discussion group have a cuppa – Robin with Tim Meagher, Denis Large and Liam Leahy.

Farm management

No two farms are the same; they may vary in terms of soil type, layout, size, financial status, handling and housing facilities or topography. Equally, no two farmers are the same, in terms of background, education, age, health, physique or mindset. Furthermore, no two years are the same, due to variations in the physical climate and the economic climate.

Therefore, while there may be plenty of books dealing with individual enterprises the overall management of each farm is quite unique.

"I suppose it's something that develops over the years," says a usually articulate Robin, more in hope than with confidence that this is an adequate description of how the farm is managed.

"What you did last year might not work this year at all, while something that failed last year could, with just a bit of tweaking, prove to be a success. It is one of the things that makes farming interesting and sometimes challenging," he adds, warming a little to the subject. "The day you become afraid to make mistakes is the day you stop learning."

As outlined earlier, Robin looks after the practical work involved in running the farm whereas, except for pulling a bit of ragwort (in season) and occasionally being called on to block a gap (when moving cattle), I concentrate mostly on paperwork and administration. The big decisions are made jointly.

"I'd like to feel that I am rewarded for what I do, but I'm not driven by money," says Robin. "I certainly have no interest in stockpiling it. I love farming and I've found a system that I like – working with cows and calves. I have no desire to own the biggest or the plushest tractor."

He has to be one of the few people who has never done the Lotto, because of "the off-chance that I might actually win... in case it might change the things that really matter, like how you see your friends and how they see you."

At this stage in our farming life we are not contemplating any major change to our farming system and Robin's ambition is quite simple: "to hopefully do a little better every year; things like getting a higher percentage of cows in calf, more calves on the ground and a higher percentage of quality stock to sell. Whether it's trying to increase returns or cut costs, there's always room for improvement."

On this farm, as on most farms, the minutiae of daily operations are all planned by, and contained in, the individual farmer's head.

Liam Leahy, Tim Meagher, Denis Large, Denis Minogue of Teagasc and Robin.

Such detail is never written down on paper. You just do the essentials and the day quickly fills itself.

One way in which we differ from the majority of farms is that most of the routine work is done during office hours, between 9am and 5pm on weekdays and between 9 am and 1pm on Saturdays, because we are lucky enough to have someone employed here. Robin works Sundays on his own.

Robin belongs to a discussion group, the IQ, and nobody has more influence on what we do in terms of the management of the farm, both day-to-day and longer-term, than its fellow members.

The group was originally set up in 1998 following a study tour to Australia organised by Richard Keenan & Co. The participants included farmers John Tait from Midleton, Co Cork, Tim Meagher from Roscrea, Co Tipperary, and Denis Large from Urlingford. On return home, a few of the participants from the midlands and Cork came together to form an informal discussion group. Then, the following year, John Tait won the inaugural Eurosuckler competition and Robin was runner-up. Shortly afterwards, Tim Meagher rang Robin and asked if the group could visit the farm. On foot of the visit, they asked him if he would like to join them.

Since then, the circumstances and the focus of some of the members have changed and, along with Robin, the core now comprises Denis Large, Tim Meagher and Liam Leahy of Woodsgift, Co Kilkenny.

"If there's a problem, the first port of call is a parley with the lads," says Robin. "Each member of the group has his strengths and, as well as pooling information and ideas, we draw on one another's experience. If it's something about tillage, I'll probably ring Liam. If it's to do with grass management, I'll contact Tim, and if it's an animal health issue, I'll talk to Denis.

A key feature of the group's activities is what they call their "run-arounds", which they carry out a few times a year. This involves all members of the group visiting each other's farms on the same designated afternoon, so that they can see everybody else's stock under the same conditions. This run-around system works for them because there are only four of them.

The run-arounds involve a full and frank discussion on site about what each of the other members is doing, or thinking of doing. The conversation is then continued over a bite to eat around someone's kitchen table.

"I would bounce critical decisions off the rest of the group," says Robin. "They will inevitably highlight aspects that you may not even have considered." These sessions never fail to throw up some issue for some member of the group and, on the advice of the others, they will change something slightly. Examples of this might be tweaking a feeding regime or taking some paddocks out of the rotation.

A friend of ours once came along on one of the run-arounds and was taken aback at their candour. "It's little we don't know about one another's business at this stage," says Robin.

"There will often be robust exchanges between us but I don't ever remember an angry word being spoken. We trust each other implicitly and the aim is to help rather than to knock. I can only speak for myself but I have always found any criticism to be helpful."

The process works because they are not in competition; their objective is to support each other. The talk is in specifics rather than generalities. There are a lot of calls to "back up there for a minute", "get out the calculator and do the sums", "so what's the answer to my question?" along with the occasional expletive or sarcastically laughing chorus of "Oh, you're right there, Robin, yeah, you're right!"

The dream

Along with some 500 million other people around the world I watched the 2012 Aintree Grand National on television. With a mile to go, my pulse was beginning to race as I watched a horse named Sunnyhillboy travelling smoothly on the outside, out of trouble, bang in contention.

My interest in him is that he is a half-brother

Frosty graze. Twinkle makes a path through the frosty grass.

to a mare we bought in 2006 named Toil and Trouble, pet name Twinkle. She is from the family of Whitbread winner Brown Windsor, and we paid 10,000 guineas for her when she was in foal to Helissio. The following spring she had a colt foal, which made 8,200 guineas that autumn. The demand for him was boosted by the fact that the aforementioned Sunnyhillboy had made a winning debut the day before.

Unfortunately, Twinkle failed to go in foal that year... and the next... and the next... and the next. Finally, after four years empty (not producing a foal) she kept the pregnancy and duly foaled in June, a filly, by the Sadler's Wells horse Well Chosen.

As I watched the Grand National I was aware that Sunnyhillboy could run a bit erratically on occasion but this time everything was going smoothly. I knew that JP McManus and Jonjo O'Neill held him in high regard and had laid him out for this race and that his jockey, Richie McLernon, got on well with him.

At the final fence, Sunnyhillboy drew alongside the leader and as he was pushed clear at the Elbow I was off the couch roaring in encouragement and excitement. However, he was being chased hard by the grey horse Neptune Collonges, the gap closing stride by stride. They flashed by the post as one but the photo showed that the grey had just edged his head in front.

It was an awful way to lose and some well-meaning friends suggested that after four-and-a-half miles a dead heat would have been the fairest result. But I have always felt that if the judge can call a winner, he should and this

You scratch my back, I'll scratch yours

outcome did not change my view; the winning distance was the tightest possible, a nose. The record books show that Neptune Collonges won the 2012 Grand National and few people will remember the horse that finished second.

I was sorely disappointed while of course acknowledging that my fleeting feelings in no way compared with those of the real connections (particularly given the additional tragic loss of Synchronised). But at this point I realised I would have felt even worse if we had sold the mare off and the horse had subsequently won. In such circumstances, there would be no chance of us ever receiving anything in terms of reflected glory. After all, Sunnyhillboy could have another go at winning the National or he might even win some other big race.

The dream is dead, long live hope.

PS. Sunnyhillboy reappeared in the 2013 running of the Grand National where he unseated his rider at the last fence when he was tailed off from the rest of the field.

PPS. But hope still lives on.

Dainty cowslips bloom in Ballygeehan.

A mother's love.

Rainy Weather.

Moorhen chicks take to the water.

Limousin bull, 'Clicker' grazes in Tentore.

May

At one point this month, it looks likely that the loader will be turning right at the exit of the avenue to the road in order to bring last year's silage to cattle in the field, while at the same time tractors and silage trailers will be turning left towards Coolderry to pick up next year's crop.

Luckily, record growth kicks in to save our blushes.

Yield for the early first-cut silage is lower than we hoped for but on the other hand the first-cut silage should make excellent feeding for the fattening cattle during the winter.

Meanwhile, our current crop of beef cattle continues to be sold from the shed at record prices.

Towards the end of the month, we enjoy a (short) spell of warm sunny weather; in the lifting dew of the early mornings the birds sing brighter and the honeysuckle smells sweeter.

Costs: *from mating to 'ate'-ing*

Production costs are critical to the success or failure of a farming enterprise, and the horsemeat-in-burgers scandal which hit Europe this past spring has generated increased public interest in the issue. Therefore I feel it would be remiss of me not to include some details about the level and composition of farming production costs. In preparing this section of the book I asked Robin for his help in trying to itemise how much it would cost to raise a theoretical calf.

For the sake of this exercise, let's call the calf Oscar.

A stock bull would be expected to sire 40 calves a year for six years, i.e. a total of about 240 calves in his lifetime. The average cost of keep at grass is €0.35/day, and the bull would spend eight months of the year at grass (0.35 X 30 days X 8 months = €84.00). The other four months would be spent in the shed at a cost of €2.40/day (2.40 X 30 X 4 = €288). His hooves would be trimmed twice a year (€80.00) and his veterinary costs (including leptospirosis vaccine, annual treatment for fluke and worms and annual TB test) would come to around €20.00.

Still with me? So the direct keep costs of a stock bull per year would be €472, the total for six years coming to €2,832. Add on the purchase price, €4,000, subtract the cull value of the bull, say €1,200, which leaves the total cost of keeping a bull for six years at €5,632 (€2,832 + €4,000 - €1,200). Divide this cost among the total number of calves he produces

The breeding season begins. Stock bull 'Alo' with heifers.

puts the cost of siring Oscar, the bull cost per calf, at about €23.50.

We then repeated the exercise for the cow, taking her purchase price (our replacements cost €910 in 2012) and estimating her keep from the time the previous calf was weaned until Oscar was weaned the following year.

In addition to the costs incurred for the bull, the suckler cow would also receive a trace element bolus and a vaccine (in order to prevent Oscar from getting scour). We would expect each cow to have in the region of eight to nine calves, and the salvage value of the cow would be about €1,400. The calculations showed that the cow cost per calf was around €335.

However, because conventional wisdom puts the actual cost of keeping a suckler cow for a year is around €600, we realised that the method of quantifying costs described above is actually oversimplified. Not all bulls are this fertile, not all cows have this number of calves, some animals have far higher veterinary costs, and some die. It became apparent, therefore, that the only way to identify the real cost was

Hopefully this might be the result...

... then this...

to use the figures from the farm accounts, which show the actual cost per kilo of beef produced.

The three major costs on our farm are feed, fertiliser and seed, and contracting. These costs combined account for two-thirds of total expenditure. Our other main costs include wages, the running of machinery and veterinary expenses (including veterinary products). There are also additional costs such as machinery depreciation. While Oscar, obviously, does not directly use machinery, a fraction of the depreciation cost of the machinery must, nevertheless, be apportioned to him.

When all the relevant costs were totted up and divided by the actual amount of beef produced on the farm during the year, we arrived at a figure of €3.70/kg. I then looked at the beef factory returns which showed that the actual price paid for the beef was €3.60/kg. This is a net loss of 10c/kg. Therefore, if Oscar weighed 400kg carcase weight and sold for €1,600, the actual cost of getting him to market would be €1,640.

This is no more than a statement of fact. Without the Single Farm Payment, we would have no income, and we are not alone in this. Most farmers would be using at least part of their SFP to run their business; many would be using all of it.

The Teagasc profit monitor results for 2011 for the BETTER Farm beef programme (involving 35 privately owned, well-managed, demonstration farms) show that the average liveweight/ha yield for 2011 was 598kg which, interestingly, turns out to be exactly the same figure as for our farm (with no adjustment for marginal land). In 2012, our liveweight output per ha was 606kg (compared to 680kg on the BETTER farms) and liveweight output per livestock unit was 366kg, compared to 351kg.

The point I am trying to make is that our farm is not too "flabby". We are very cost conscious and are always looking at ways to reduce costs without cutting corners, so as to avoid compromising animal welfare or meat quality.

In terms of contracting, for example, there is very little we can do, as we have no intention

... and finally this.

of investing in a lot of machinery. However, by reseeding pastures and using better varieties of grass we could potentially grow more grass using less fertiliser, thus spending less without reducing output. An ambitious aspiration? Maybe. But if you don't set goals you'll never reach them.

Cattle deaths

There is a rural tale about a widow who lived alone on a mountain with nothing other than a nanny goat for company or income. Then the goat died. To a neighbour offering his condolences, she stoically said: "Ah sure, where you have livestock, you have dead stock".

Around 3% of the cattle on our farm die over the course of every year. Strikingly, this figure never varies much, irrespective of the weather, or our efforts to do anything differently or any other factor.

As with other species, including humans, one of the most dangerous times is around birth – just before, during and in the first days afterwards. This is especially so for calves but

Cow found dead in field, from grass tetany.

also for cows. We lose between 1% and 2% of calves in the first 28 days of life (compared with the national average for beef herds of 5-6%).

When the calving season is tailing off there are inevitably one or two losses and these may be caused by a lack of concentration or tiredness. While 28 days is a recognised milestone in the life of a newborn, there will always be a few "creaking doors" – animals that may have survived an earlier challenge but that never reach full health and inevitably succumb to something further down the line. In calves, the main causes of death are either dietary (e.g. scour) or respiratory (e.g. pneumonia).

Sometimes a death may occur without any warning, such as when a cow gets grass tetany. Occasionally, there may be an outbreak of disease, as happened in January 2012 when we lost an 18-month-old bull as a result of infectious bovine rhinotracheitis (IBR).

Then, there are accidents. One morning in December Robin found a calf lying dead in the shed. He looked completely normal and displayed no sign of injury. It is likely that a cow, possibly his mother or another cow, may have laid down too close to him and smothered him.

It might seem unfeeling to be talking of deaths as "losses" and "percentages" but we don't take them lightly. In reality, we do everything we can to keep an animal alive regardless of the cost. But if an animal dies despite our best efforts to keep it alive, we accept it.

In fact, the one thing that would really annoy Robin is if he failed to recognise a problem or

Sad sight. Cow licks her calf which is suffering from white muscle disease, a disorder caused by selenium deficiency and she has to be subsequently euthanased.

did not take corrective action in time to save the animal. In such a circumstance it would not be the economic loss that would bother him but the feeling that he had failed to do everything possible to ensure that the animal had the chance to live and reach its full potential.

In 2003, our daughter Rachel was stillborn at full term. At the time we were hand-rearing four motherless calves. A little white half-twin named Rings, so-called because of the red, circular patches around both eyes, had pneumonia. As I walked down the yard the day after Rachel's funeral, I could hear Rings' laboured breathing from a distance. He was stretched flat out under an infra-red lamp and seemed to be drifting from one side to the other of the line between life and death. Despite his own horrific personal loss, Robin was doing everything possible to save the calf which, in time, recovered.

A leveret.

New bull arrives – 'Court Drew' (by Empire D'Ochain/EZN)

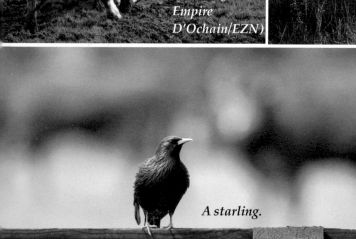

A starling.

Girls play in the rain.

Robin turns the hay.

Calladines spray paint the straw shed.

June

This month, we manage to cut the main crop of silage during a spell of nice weather but then the skies open before we have a chance to bring it all in. It then rains non-stop for the following 24 hours and well over a full week passes before the silage pit is finally covered.

We spread some fertiliser on the first fields that are cut for silage and as soon as this greens up we wean the oldest bull calves that are targeted for sale live.

A brief period of respite is followed by more heavy rain.

We manage to cut some hay but it is slow to dry due to the lack of sunshine.

Twinkle has a filly foal.

Silage and hay

The appointed time arrives. Where is he? Is that a drop of rain I feel? Look out up at the sky, go back to what you were doing, check the yard again, sssh, cock your ear, is that a big machine coming down the road, is it slowing? Yes, no, it's gone by, wasn't the right engine anyway; unable to do anything except wait, you head indoors, check the barometer, it's gone from Fair to Change, uh oh, look out the window, pick up the newspaper, flick to the weather forecast, "cloudy but mainly dry", look out the window again, a different side of the house this time, more clouds here but not as dark. Maybe it will hold, check the clock, then the mobile, maybe he rang… or even texted or, failing all that, maybe there's a missed call on the landline. And on it goes.

All this can only mean one thing: it's silage time. Despite a widespread perception to the contrary, farmers tend to be a fairly positive bunch. Whether it's sowing seeds, milking cows or lambing ewes, our lives are intrinsically intertwined with nature, and the perpetual wonder of it all inevitably rubs off on us and sustains us.

However, when it comes to cutting the silage, few farmers escape the strain. The

Filling the pit in ideal conditions.

entire process is one of unrelenting pressure, beginning even before the mower takes to the field and continuing through the various stages – tossing out the grass, turning it back into rows, picking it up in the field, dropping it in the yard, filling the pit and covering it.

Silage-making is one of the most important annual jobs on a livestock farm. While other activities such as breeding, calving and cattle sales occur over an extended period, silage is made in just a few short days and a successful outcome is dependent on the prevailing weather during that time. A further complication is the fact that most farmers, like ourselves, hire a contractor to do the silage-making and, when the weather is favourable, everybody wants theirs done at exactly the same time. This can lead to difficulty in finding

Tea in the meadow. Robin and Ruth enjoy the first (and, almost, last) picnic of the summer.

Silage lying in water.

a contractor who's available when you want one.

One of the reasons we started to grow maize was to bulk up our winter fodder as a substitute for a second crop of grass silage. This was because the older pastures from which we had been taking the second cut of silage were not up to the task of providing two viable cuts of grass. Most of the farm has been re-seeded in recent times and we have found that the new pastures are capable of producing a second cut that is almost on a par with the first cut.

Consequently, for the first time in a number of years we took an early cut of silage in mid-May which, given the absence of maize from our crop rotation, we hoped would make good quality forage for finishing cattle next spring. Thankfully, this went to plan. The sun shone, the trailers left clouds of dust in their wake, there was even a chance for a family picnic.

The very next day my camera had a lucky escape. I went off in the jeep to take some silage photos in a field down Coolderry Lane. Ruth had fallen asleep and still was when I had completed my business so I parked the camera on the bonnet to avoid disturbing her by opening a door. I then made a phonecall before suddenly realising it was time to pick up Sarah from school. I hopped in the jeep and took off up the lane and down the road. I was picking up speed when a thought jumped into my mind: the camera! There it was, still perched precariously on the bonnet, within reach (except for the small matter of the windscreen in between). My instinct was to jam on the brakes but something made me realise that this would make the camera shoot off. So I eased my foot off the pedal and we slowly came to a halt. Miraculously it had never moved. I felt such an idiot.

It was a different story weatherwise a fortnight later when it came to the main part of the first cut. Despite an ominous weather forecast, Robin cut the silage on the June Bank Holiday Monday. He was out until 11o'clock that night shaking it out to help it dry. On the Wednesday morning they started picking it up and it looked as though they just might escape when the skies opened and the downpour began.

A month's rain fell in the following two days. Some of the silage that still had to be picked up was in Tentore and part of the field ended up under water. It was difficult to look out and see sheets of rain falling on the pit, knowing there was nothing we could do about it.

Robin remained positive throughout and when the weather finally dried up and we got to finish the pit on the Saturday he said he had often made worse silage in better conditions. While there was a lot of liquid running off the pit he was convinced that this was mostly rainwater, not effluent.

We took the second cut in early August and the most remarkable thing about that event was that it was unremarkable – cut dry, turned twice, picked up a few days later and safely landed in the pit.

Unfortunately, Robin's optimism about the main first cut proved unfounded. When the silage was analysed in September, it was very low in protein and dry matter. Thankfully, however, for some reason it seemed to be quite palatable, which at least meant that the animals didn't turn up their noses at it and we were able to add a bit of soya and molasses to provide more energy and protein.

Even though the early first cut yielded around 30% less in terms of bulk than the main first cut, it actually generated €100 per acre more on a feed value basis. So, the lesson for the future is that we will really have to look at cutting our silage a few weeks earlier than normal.

During the run-up to calving, we feed hay to the cows. Saving the hay proved every bit as stressful as saving the silage, with even more mixed results. We cut one field in the last week of June and it rotted. The valuable lesson we learnt for the future was that, if the forecast is not good and we have "hay" that's pretty close to ready, we should bale it and wrap it. Fortunately, at the end of July we managed to get another field saved in ideal conditions, and, while the hay might not have had maximum nutritional value, it suited its intended purpose perfectly.

Loughabarra

Loughabarra is described in John Feehan's *Environmental History of Laois* (1983) as "an interesting and varied habitat… (with) a large bird population relative to its size".

It still attracts winter visiting ducks but not geese in the same kinds of numbers as in the past. Among the other birds we now see in Loughabarra are Snipe, Kestrel, Meadow Pipit, Linnet, Wheatear, Willow Warbler and a lone

A view of the open water in Loughabarra.

Buzzard.

Hardly a week goes by during the grazing season when Robin doesn't comes home with a "you should have been there with your camera" story, like the one about the pair of brightly coloured cock pheasants fighting or the mallard duck leading her new hatchlings across a field to water. But topping the list is the buzzard, with various versions of how "he landed feet away". There used to be a pair of them and over the years I have seen them in the distance but, despite making a number of trips to Tentore in 2012 for the sole purpose of snapping the remaining him/her, the only time I ever got close was the day it spent several minutes circling overhead. This was, of course, on a day I was herding with Robin… and had left the camera at home. Murphy's Law!

Old maps show an earlier road connecting Ballacolla to Clough, passing through the northern fringes of Loughabarra. The area was also used as a drinking point for local farm animals; while Eamon Fitzpatrick in neighbouring Kilminfoyle would, when he was growing up, have heard references to turf being cut there.

Eamon believes the turf may have been finally exhausted during World War I, having previously being worked during the Great Famine in the 1840s – a period when the area around Kilminfoyle and over towards Dairyhill was densely populated.

Over the years, various efforts have been made to drain Loughabarra so as to prevent flooding of the surrounding pasture land. These efforts have met with only limited success.

A pair of summer visitor Wheatears.

So now, this rare landscape and its living inhabitants combine to create a fairytale atmosphere and we feel lucky to have such a special treasure practically on our doorstep.

A wetland jewel

By Dr Fiona MacGowan, ecologist

In a landscape dominated by intensive agriculture, Loughabarra is a wetland biodiversity jewel tucked away in the southwestern corner of Laois.

In the past, wetland areas were common in

Ecologist, Dr Fiona MacGowan, undertakes plant survey of Loughabarra.

our damp corner of Europe. Now, however, due to drainage work they are much rarer and are therefore becoming increasingly important as refuges for species of wildlife unseen in other habitats.

By their nature, wetlands impose different and difficult conditions on the plants and animals they host. Clearly they are wet, but they can be acidic bogs or alkaline fens. Also, they can be flooded at some periods and not at others. These conditions mean that the plant species in particular have to be specialised and this is why most are not found in more common habitats such as hedgerows and agricultural grassland.

The wet conditions lead to the dominance of grass-like plants such as rushes and sedges, with a sprinkling of shrubbery in the form of willows and alders. Insect life abounds, with dragonflies, damselflies, butterflies and moths galore. Moreover, in the pattern of the great web of life, the diversity of insects also brings a diversity of birds who know this is a good place to feed.

At present, Loughabarra would be

Dr Fiona MacGowan and her husband Dr Mark McCorry.

Skull-cap.

technically termed a 'wet grassland with elements of fen and scrub'. In time, depending on the underlying hydrology, it may develop into more of a fen or it may develop into scrub woodland.

The accompanying photographs show two plants which are only occasionally found in Ireland; both of these plants thrive in Loughabarra. The delicate mauve-flowered Skull-cap (*Scuttellaria galericulata*), so-called as

its cap-like flowers resemble the leather caps Roman soldiers wore under their helmets, and Buckthorn (*Rhamnus cathartica*), a small tree adapted to growing in places that seasonally flood – something that would kill off many other tree species.

Buckthorn.

Top cow, No. 49, with her 2011 bull calf.

Bill McEvoy, *builder*

When I suggest to Bill McEvoy of Oldtown Construction that he is a perfectionist, he chuckles. Then his expression quickly turns serious and he gives what is surely the ultimate perfectionist's answer: "Well, I try to be."

He chuckles a lot but this belies an incisive mind and other attributes that have made Oldtown Construction the best in the business, and him a pillar (sorry!) of the community. Politely spoken and quietly proud of his work, he is a good listener and organiser, a hard worker and a big supporter of the GAA

Bill McEvoy grew up on a small farm in Rapla, Rathdowney, where he still lives. After finishing primary school he was kept at home to help out on the farm. But building rather than farming was in his blood – his grandfather and namesake used to build cottages for the County Council – and when the opportunity arose Bill joined Keenan Bros Construction in Carlow in the late 1960s.

Bill struck out on his own in 1977 and Oldtown Construction was established the following year. In its early days, the company focused on the agricultural sector and then gradually expanded into doing some industrial construction as well as the occasional one-off house. During the Celtic Tiger years, it even built an entire housing estate.

In the boom years, Oldtown employed 40 people but today that figure is around the 18 mark. Bill feels a strong sense of loyalty to his workers. This loyalty is mutual and several of his employees have been with him for over 20

Bill McEvoy.

years. They stayed with him during the boom when, as he readily acknowledges, they could have made more money elsewhere. It comes as no surprise therefore that he hates having to make any of his employees redundant.

Each year, Oldtown does between 55 and 60 jobs, all of which are in the agricultural sector or are agriculture-related. The strongest demand is from dairy farmers who are gearing up for increasing production post-2015. "There

is a decent share of work," says Bill, "but it's highly competitive so you have to price down to the last bolt. In a recession the boss works harder."

Styles of building obviously reflect changes in farming practice. As a result, Bill has witnessed the move from haybarns to silage pits and, as a result of increasing intensification of animal production, slatted houses that in recent years have much higher roofs in order to maximise air circulation.

At a social level, he sees first-hand the increasing isolation of farmers. "They're mad for a chat when they come on the phone. There was a time if you were doing something as minor as putting up a shelf in someone's house, half the parish would troop in. Today on the other hand the neighbours would barely comment, no matter the size of the job. Farmers go to the mart for someone to talk to… and the dairy fellas don't even have that."

Now in his mid 60s, Bill has no plans to retire but two of his sons, Kieran and Liam (both engineers and settled locally) are involved in the business. The one thing he would love to do is spend more time out on site. He misses the hands-on side of things as well as building-site humour.

As to the why such a bawdy brand of wit is intrinsically linked with the construction business, Bill ends the interview as he began, with a chuckle: "It's hard physical work… and I suppose humour helps us to get each other through the day."

Bill checks the measurements.

Arriving for work. Oldtown workers, Larry Dunphy, (open with the company since 1984), Anthony McEvoy, Kazi Kowalski, know as 'Kaji', from Poland, opens his top button.

Joe Hyland chats with Bill.

Bill measures the resurfaced yard.

Bill McEvoy.

Joe Hyland, *farm worker*

Largely as a consequence of mechanisation and reduced farm incomes, most farmers in Ireland now work on their own. Robin and I are very lucky that our farming operation is of a sufficiently large scale to enable us to employ somebody full-time. Our farm worker, Joe Hyland, has been with us since 2008.

Joe was born in Aghaboe and now lives just a few kilometres away, which is handy both for him and for us. It means he can nip home quickly, if necessary. Conversely, he can be here in minutes if something urgent crops up outside working hours. Fortunately, this does not happen very often; nonetheless, Joe voluntarily asserts that he is "on call day or night".

He inherited the 54-acre family farm and he also rents 20 acres which, since the demise of the sugar beet industry, has operated a store-to-beef system. His animals are managed in the opposite pattern to ours: he feeds them in the evening and checks them, then in the morning he gives them a bit of meal before coming here.

The Charolais stores are bought at 18 months and finished at under 30 months. During the winter he also raises 25 suck calves, feeding them milk replacer. (It takes a 25kg bag of replacer to rear a calf.) He then holds the calves for the summer before selling them on to buy-in stores.

After attending Clough Primary School and St Fergal's College in Rathdowney, Joe went to Ballyhaise Agricultural College for a year and was kept on for a further 18 months after that,

"working with pigs, mushrooms, feeding cattle, dairying, lambing, whatever was needed."

He then spent five years milking cows with the Farm Relief Service before going to work for Tom Hennessy of Manor Stone Quarries. So, while it was "mostly feeding and handling cattle, there was also a bit of stone work. I was never idle."

After a few years trying to manage without a full-time person during the height of the Celtic Tiger years (a period when we couldn't get anybody suitable to take on the job), Joe saw our ad in the local paper. "It said a 'beef farm' in Ballacolla and I knew straight away it was here," he says.

Other than having the obvious cattle and machinery-handling skills, Joe is trustworthy, a good timekeeper and conscientious – characteristics which are very important to us.

"When you working closely with someone every day, trust is critical," says Robin. "It just wouldn't work out and you would get nothing done if, for example, you had to step away every time you needed to make or take a business call."

As for time-keeping, I have to admit that it is more important to Robin than to me. And he is better at it. I'm the one who arrives bang on the button or even a minute late, while Robin would always allow plenty of time if he was going somewhere. And he never lets me forget how I kept him waiting for almost half an hour on our wedding day... or how he really started

to sweat under the collar when he overheard one guest whisper to his neighbour, "I wonder if we'll still get fed if she doesn't turn up." Now, if we are travelling together somewhere, I make it my business to get ready that bit earlier... and I admit that there is a lot to be said for being able to travel with ease... but on my own I always revert to cutting things tight.

"Punctuality is important in everything," says Robin. "It's about courtesy and respect as well as the obvious matter of getting the job done. In any job if you are consistently late you will get your knuckles rapped. It should be no different in farming. A business is a business.

"Maybe it's because there have always been men employed here but we tend to have a structure to the day, a start time and a finish time. We don't keep going until we get fed up or get tired."

In Robin's schooldays there would still have been three men working here. Many of the men who worked here down through the years were here for a long time: Ben Kavanagh, who died in 2013, for over 25 years and Jim Tuck even longer. Pam says: "From our point of view, there was never a problem with anyone and as far as I know they never left discontented, It was on account of their age, or maybe they were going to a better job."

From the very first conversation I had with Robin I noticed that when he spoke about the farm it was in terms of "we". I initially, and disappointedly, assumed this referred to himself and the missus so I was mightily

Multi-skilled Joe does some welding.

Joe unhitches feeder trailer in Tentore.

Joe clips a heifers tail to prevent a build-up of excess dirt while indoors.

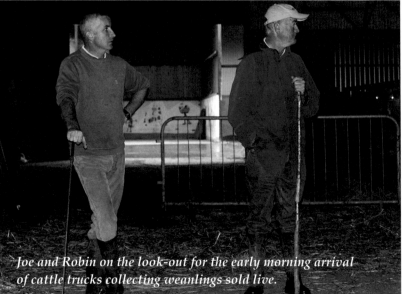

Joe and Robin on the look-out for the early morning arrival of cattle trucks collecting weanlings sold live.

Joe Hyland.

relieved to discover it referred to whoever was working here as well as himself and Pam (the family) ... which now includes myself and the girls. "I always see it as working together, a team," says Robin. "It's not quite governing by consensus, because someone has to be the boss, to take responsibility for making decisions, but two heads are better than one and I would like to think that the person you work with feels parts of those decisions.

"I would always treat people with respect and never ask someone to do something I wasn't willing to do myself. In turn, I would like to think that I am easy to work for. But if I thought that someone was taking

Padraig Murphy and Joe usher cattle along the farm roadway.

Joe mows the silage while Robin tosses it out to help it dry faster.

advantage of that, they wouldn't last long here."

For his part, Joe gets satisfaction from his work. A simple example: if he has a spare minute he will put the mechanical brush on the teleporter and be off cleaning the yard. He would never need to be asked. "It's not a big job to do it and it's the first thing you see when you come in the gate." He adds, "Everything is well-kept here; there is no hardship except anything you might bring on yourself."

It's obvious that Joe enjoys where he works and takes pride in it, which is nice for him and nice for us.

Ten-month old heifers enjoy a summer graze.

Edwina Farrell, *horse vet*

Edwina Farrell must be one of the few people in Ireland to have welcomed the recession. As a direct result of the recession, her business has become more streamlined, regular and manageable.

Edwina is a horse vet.

During the boom, horse racing in general and the thoroughbred breeding sector in particular experienced exponential growth. Many property developers and others in the construction industry built stable yards and got into breeding as well as racing. In 2007, over 12,500 foals were registered in Ireland. This fell to 7,500 by 2010 and has remained at that level.

After the bust, Edwina was left with a number of outstanding debts, some of which are being pursued through legal channels. She is not bitter about this; rather, she feels that she is actually in a better place. "I tend to think that things happen for a reason. I don't want to sound cocky but I now have an established group of good, regular clients."

The work is less frenetic and she has become established as a sole, ambulatory practitioner.

Edwina, who is from a farming family in nearby Durrow, has always loved horses and like many young girls she also dreamed of achieving success as a professional rider, an eventer in her case. By the time the Leaving Cert came around, this had morphed into a desire to become a vet. She was offered a place to study medicine but as the points for the veterinary course were higher she decided to repeat her Leaving Cert year – much to her dad's horror. "What do you want to be a vet for?"

"I think GP work would be awful," says Edwina. "Anyway, as lots of people would attest, my bedside manner is more suitable to animals, and yes I can be a bit blunt," she adds with a laugh.

She qualified in 1995, struck out on her own in 2006 and has found that being a woman is not an obstacle to success in a horse veterinary practice. "In fact, in certain cases female vets are preferred to male vets as they are considered more thorough and caring. As a rule of thumb, I suppose you could say it's boys for treating lameness and girls for mares and foals."

There have always been horses here at Coole but the thoroughbreds coincided with my arrival on the farm. Edwina started coming here when we needed to have a mare checked for pregnancy and the farm vet, Dan Delahunty (now retired), didn't have an ultrasound scanner.

Edwina works long hours (starting at 5.30am in the spring) but fortunately she doesn't have to do a lot of night work. The one thing she dreads is a call to attend a foaling, which happens a couple of times a year. There is a logic to her dread. Most of her clients are people with a lot of mares who are well-used to foaling them, or they are livestock farmers who are used to cows calving. "So if they do call you out, you know it is serious. If a caesarean is required, the likelihood is that you would not carry out this operation in a field. Whereas with a cow, you could do that.

"Equines are far more susceptible to peritonitis infections compared to the bovine; also they have to get a general anaesthetic whereas caesareans on cows are performed while they are standing. The other factor is the higher perceived monetary or otherwise value of the mare."

She contends that vets in mixed practice are actually better at foaling, because they do more animal deliveries generally. Would she like to work in mixed practice herself? "Not for diamonds," she asserts, "because of the nature of the business – it's very physical, often outdoors, the repetitiveness of testing, dirty yards... and dirty (spattered) faces." Neither does she believe that a small animal practice would give her the same satisfaction that she gets from horses.

For Edwina, the highs of the job are getting a tricky mare to go in foal or seeing a sick foal recover and then go on to achieve success in the sales ring or on the racetrack. Conversely, the lows are when an animal dies or has to be put down. "I am not an animal lover in the cuddly, cuddly sense. But I do love them. When I was starting working and would see an animal dying, I used to cry." Indeed, the first time she had to put down a horse she had a nightmare. "I have become more objective. You have to be… otherwise you couldn't do this job."

Modern horse-owners are demanding. They

Edwina checks out Twinkle's new foal.

Edwina Farrell.

Edwina prepares an injection.

Edwina does the paperwork.

ask lots of questions and they are very well informed. They expect high standards, almost instant diagnostic results and access to the best equipment. One particular machine that Edwina has cost €60,000 (and it already needs to be upgraded!). In addition, the nature of the breeding business has changed.

All the stud preparation work is now done at home and the mares are then transported to the stud for "walk-on" covers. As a result, the timing of the preparation has to be precise. This preparation involves checking the health of the mare's uterus, then tracking the mare's follicular activity to identify the best time to be mated with the stallion. On return from stud, the mare is checked for ovulation. 15 days later she is scanned and is, hopefully, pregnant.

Occasionally, Edwina accompanies stallions shuttling between the Northern Hemisphere and the Southern Hemisphere for the alternating breeding seasons. "Usually the flights are uneventful but these are very valuable animals and there is always a chance of something major going wrong. So it does push up the cost of my professional indemnity insurance… but the trips are a bit of fun."

Edwina writes out a schedule for her working day but the schedule often goes haywire. Such unpredictability does not bother her; she (usually) enjoys "life on the edge." One of the downsides of this unpredictability, and the fact that she works on her own, is the impact it has on her social life. "I don't get much time off, but the people I work with are very sociable. When you love the work you do, you don't feel like you're missing out." After a pause, she adds: "I know, I'm sad, amn't I?" From the contented look on her face she clearly feels anything but.

Up early, Twinkle with her filly foal.

The Jane Austen Connection

Heading out of Ballacolla village towards Rathdowney, on land that Talbots know as 'Briggs' but which is also known locally as 'Caldbecks', is the site of the former Ballacolla House. I thought it would be interesting to include a couple of lines about the prominent professional family who once lived here. Instead, once I started researching, I found myself on a riveting foray into local and literary history.

William Caldbeck, who died in 1869 aged 95, is described on his gravestone, a couple of fields away in Killermogh, as Clerk of the Peace for Queens County for many years. At the time of Griffith's Valuation, he was renting almost 160 acres from John W Fitzpatrick and was himself landlord of some 124 acres of land in Ballacolla along with a range of buildings/offices which included a dispensary, Petit Session house and a police barracks among a number of other properties in the county.

His son, Richard Thomas, a magistrate/solicitor, married Mary Costello, eldest daughter of Charles Hely of Foulks Court, High Sheriff of Kilkenny. She died in 1869, aged 33. Known as Mary Costello Caldbeck, she wrote a novel called *Sefton Hall* which was published posthumously in 1870. As part of a scheme to publish major and minor novels, it was republished in 2011.

Richard remarried in 1873, to Mary Anne (Maimie) Greer from Scotland. Richard died in 1895. The 1901 Census records Ballacolla House as having 23 rooms with 14 windows at the front of the house, and the head of the family as 47-year-old Mary (Maimie) and her children, Alice (24), Amy (22) and Richard C (16).

Richard trained as an electrical engineer, married in London in 1909 and was a member of the Royal Engineers or Sappers in WWI. An older son named Eaton fought in the Boer War in the Siege of Ladysmith and died in the Adelaide Hospital in Dublin in 1908. Amy had died in 1906.

By 1911, the census shows Frances Alice Minnie Caldbeck (single, farmer) as the head of household with no mention of any other family members. In 1913, she married the Rev William Bruce Briggs but died just two years later.

Frances is described on her headstone as the great great granddaughter of the Rev Edward Cooper (born 1770) of Yoxall, Staffordshire, and a Fellow of Oxford. An evangelical Anglican minister who was a noted writer of sermons and hymns including *Father, of Heaven, whose love profound* which is still in common usage, he was a first cousin and known associate of Jane Austen.

However, from references to him in her correspondence, their relationship does not appear to have been particularly warm. One of Cooper's worst offences as far as she was concerned was the habit of writing what she obviously considered to be insensitive sympathy letters. It has even been suggested that he may have partially inspired Mr Collins' character in *Pride and Prejudice*, especially in the episode where he sends a stern letter to Mr Bennet when news breaks of Lydia's elopement with Wickham.

Back entrance to the former Ballacolla House.

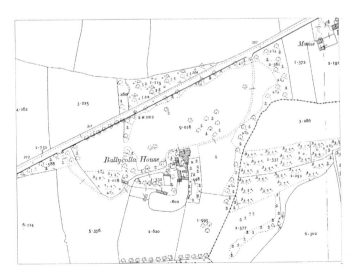

Map shows Ballacolla House as a substantial residence.

Architecture

The farm is home to a range of old structures and buildings; some of the buildings are now in ruins and others no longer exist.

A number of old buildings remain at Coole, including a stone milking byre on which the roof was recently raised to make a grain store and an older stone-and-mortar lofted barn which has been used for a wide range of activities down through the years.

In Tentore, a limekiln and old cottage are both long gone. There is still a solid stone building where workhorses were once housed and which was later used as a walk-in shelter for outwintering cattle. This building has been in a state of disuse for many years and its galvanised roof blew off in 2007.

Ballacolla House was in ruins when Bob bought the farm from Jim Cunningham in the 1950s. As was common at the time, the ruins were knocked down and buried nearby. All that remains of the house is its impressive wrought iron entrance rails and ornate cut-stone piers that bear the symbol of a knotted snake, which is thought may have a Masonic connection.

In the townland of Killermogh, accessed via a by-road we know as Coolderry Lane, lies a large trapezoidal Norman moated structure from the 13th century, close to the River Gully.

A couple of hundred metres away are the ruins of the old Killermogh church and graveyard. Dr Jack Carter, writing in *The Built Curiosities of Laois* (2012), says this is actually an early Christian site associated with a St Muicin or St Mochinus. Local legend is that this church was one of seven in the parish of Clonenagh and that it was burned down by Cromwell's soldiers. In any event, it lay in ruins in 1731.

When the church was finally rebuilt in 1796 with the aid of a grant of £500 from the Board of First Fruits, it was moved a mile or so away as the crow flies, to Rathmakelly. Apparently, this location was chosen because it was more accessible to the majority of parishioners.

The old churchyard is now overgrown but it is surrounded by a fine stone wall in relatively good condition. This has a stile and a striking entrance comprising a pair of ivy-topped cut-stone pillars and a tall iron gate which preserve a sense of dignity.

The graveyard contains some fine headstones and that of Silvester Dooley, from the early 19th century, bears the following salient entreaty:

Good travellers who chance to pass this way
Fail not for my departed soul to pray
Here also mark, perhaps know, in thy prime
The stealing steps of ever fleeting time
Thou wilt be what I am
Seize the present hour
Employ that well for that's within thy power

Old Killermogh churchyard.

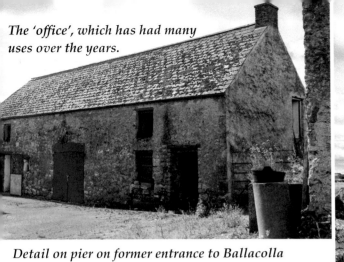

The 'office', which has had many uses over the years.

Detail on pier on former entrance to Ballacolla House.

Old shed in Tentore.

Pump at Coolderry.

Norman moated structure in Coolderry.

26/1/1941

"Sunday Independent" Special Representative

ON arrival in Ballacolla (Laoighis) yesterday I found great activity on the part of over a dozen inspectors from the Department of Agriculture; and Mr. M. A. Feehan, Co. Surveyor, was busily engaged in procuring Co. Council workers to dig a pit for the burial of the carcases of 57 cattle, 22 pigs, and 64 sheep from the farm of Mr. Peter Talbot, of the townland of Coole.

This represents Mr. Talbot's entire stock on the farm, with the exception of his horses which, not being subject to foot and mouth disease, will not be destroyed.

The cattle comprise store animals, springers, milch cows, yearlings, and calves.

The pigs include two sows, one of which was particularly valuable. Among the sheep are included lambs only a few hours old.

The Government valuer is expected to arrive shortly after which the slaughter of the animals will begin.

Meanwhile, the farm is completely isolated.

The Talbot family, who reside in a handsome two-storey house about 50 yards from the Balacolla-Durrow road, are confined to the dwelling.

Supt. T. Keyes, Abbeyleix, has about 100 extra Guards on duty day and night encircling the inner ring of an area of 15 mile radius, to see that no movement of animals takes place. A still larger force of Guards protect the outer ring, which leads into Co. Kilkenny.

Mr. Talbot is one of the most progressive farmers in this, the centre of a great cattle-rearing area. He owns 160 acres, and with his three sons tills a large acreage.

He and his family are exceedingly popular and great sympathy is extended to him.

They estimated their immediate loss in stock at about £3,000. Including the loss of milk, butter and farmyard manure, they stated that they would estimate a total loss of £4,000.

British View

The ban on the shipment of livestock from Eire to Britain owing to an outbreak of foot and mouth disease will have no immediate effect on Britain's food situation, said a Ministry of Food official in London yesterday.

He pointed out that Irish cattle are normally kept for about two months after their arrival in Britain before going to the market. Long before the two months would have elapsed the restriction on imports would doubtless be removed.

IN NORTH

All shipment of live stock from Northern Ireland has been suspended, and the Ministry of Agriculture in Belfast has cancelled the arrangements for the purchase of fat cattle and sheep at the three Belfast salesyards on Tuesday next.

The Ministry also announced the discovery of foot and mouth disease in the Dungiven district, and they have cancelled the purchase of fat cattle and sheep at Kilrea, Maghera, and Draperstown, and of five pigs at Kilrea and Maghera.

Bobby Hovenden, who turned 87 in 2012.

Cattle graze on the high moor where animals slaughtered in 1941 were buried.

Publication: Irish Press 1931-1995; Date: Jan 25, 1941; Section: None; Page Number: 8

FOOT-AND-MOUTH OUTBREAK IN MIDLANDS

Export Ban Re-Imposed

IN consequence of a foot-and-mouth disease outbreak in Laoighis the Minister for Agriculture has suspended all livestock shipments to Britain until further notice.

In a statement last night the Department of Agriculture, pointing out that the speedy eradication of the disease is a matter of national concern, urged farmers and stockowners in their own interests to render every possible assistance to the Departmental inspectors and the local gardai in securing compliance with the orders made to that end.

The outbreak occurred on the farm of Mr. Peter Talbot at Coole, about half-a-mile from Ballacolla village and about six miles from Abbeyleix. It is stated that twelve cattle are affected.

Mr. Talbot, who is an extensive farmer, is widely known as a progressive agriculturist.

When the presence of the disease was suspected on Thursday afternoon the movement of cattle in the area was immediately stopped by gardaí on the order of Supt. Keyes who had communicated with the Department of Agriculture.

Two Department inspectors arrived shortly afterwards. They returned to Dublin yesterday. Hundreds of gardaí from various Midland stations arrived last evening and last night to enforce the order prohibiting the removal of live stock from any farm within a radius of 15 miles of the farm.

Gárdaí have drawn a cordon around the area, and all the roads are patrolled.

Mr. Talbot has 62 cattle, 55 sheep and 22 pigs on the farm.

The last outbreak of foot-and-mouth disease in the Twenty-Six Counties occurred in Wexford in 1927.

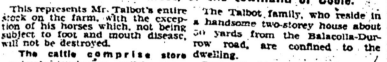

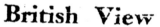

Footh-and-mouth disease 1941

The Talbot farm hit the national headlines in 1941 when it suffered the country's first outbreak of foot-and-mouth disease (FMD) in 14 years. The automatic response of the Irish Government was to suspend all livestock shipments to our largest market, Britain.

Considering the devastation that accompanied the FMD outbreak in Britain as recently as 2001, it's easy to imagine how much worse the impact on the family and the broader economy would have been 60 years earlier, given Ireland's heavy dependence on agriculture and the continuing fallout from the Economic War.

"The outbreak occurred on the farm of Mr. Peter Talbot at Coole," according to a report in the *Irish Press* dated 25 January. "Hundreds of Gardaí from various Midland stations arrived last evening… to enforce the order prohibiting the removal of livestock from any farm within a radius of 15 miles of the farm," it continues. One wonders what would have to happen today to attract "hundreds" of Gardaí.

The view locally was that FMD had been introduced to the area by a man from Scotland who had visited the farm to buy cattle. Several people described, in almost identical words, how "he put his hand on one of the animals and that beast was the first to get the disease."

The family was confined to the farm and, for weeks, Bobby Hovenden, a relation and close friend from nearby Durrow, used to bring a gallon of milk as far as the perimeter fence every day after school.

When the stock was slaughtered the *Irish Independent* reported, "Mr. Talbot is one of the most progressive farmers in the… area… and with his three sons, tills a large acreage. He and his family are exceedingly popular and great sympathy is extended to them." The language used suggests that an FMD outbreak was almost viewed in the same way as a death in the family.

The highly infectious disease did spread to the immediate area and well beyond. Hundreds of cases occurred and the details of practically all cases were reported in the national newspapers, an indication of the ongoing recognition of the serious impact of the disease in economic, human and animal terms. By year end, thanks to a policy of animal slaughter and movement restrictions, the country was again clear.

Despite the traumatic events, Bobby Hovenden says that Bob (Robin's dad) reacted promptly and turned the situation around. "They couldn't get back into cattle for six months but Bob was very driven, so once the animals were slaughtered, the farm disinfected and the main restrictions lifted, he bought four more horses, ploughed the whole place and sowed corn," said Bobby, adding, "he got a right good harvest and made a lot of money."

Bobby helped to draw the corn to Abbeyleix railway station, with the wheat going to Boland's Mill. Given that this operation took at least a week to complete and that each of ten horses was pulling a cart with 25cwt, on three trips a day, Bobby reckons that the harvest could have topped 200 tonnes.

Barley being unloaded in 2012.

Members of Laois Discussion Groups.

Robin places hay bale into feeder.

Roy Bailey.

Ruth.

Rainbow over cornfield.

Oldtown workers pull plastic over fresh concrete as skies open.

Ruth displays a homegrown raspberry.

A Meadow Pipit.

Tom Everard, Chris Daly, ICBF, Robin and Pat Donnellan, ICBF.

A beef bull.

Cows eating hay in run-up to calving.

July

All through the month of July the weather continues in the same broken pattern and the summer departs without ever really arriving.

We finally give up on our field of hay. It is rotten and unfit to be fed to anything, so we bale it up and dump it.

An Oldtown Construction team arrives to repair parts of the yard where the concrete has become broken up.

While 2012 has been an awful year for strawberries, it's been pretty good for raspberries. Every morning this month our girls race out to the garden for first pickings.

We continue to buy breeding heifers from Clare Marts. In line with beef prices, heifers are more expensive this year than other years.

Farm chorus

There is always some sound on the farm but as daybreak approaches it all begins anew as the

A Yellowhammer, now sadly increasingly rare. In Spring, male sings well-known tune, often rendered 'A little bit of bread and no cheese'.

A noisy rook.

first bird starts to sing, initially tentatively but soon with increased confidence. Others join in and it quickly crescendos to an ever-varying, always uplifting, harmony: the House Sparrow's cheery chirps, the Mistle Thrush's rattle, the Yellow Hammer's 'a little bit of bread and no cheese', the Jackdaw's sharp caw caw caw, the Wood Pigeon's coo.

The birds are either calling for a mate or warning off competitors and predators. What a happy coincidence… or clever design of nature… that songs which are so important to the birds' survival should sound to their neighbours like the merriest of tunes proclaiming a bright start to the new day, and should also have such a positive effect on our own wellbeing.

Throughout the four months of winter, and even beyond, the farmyard is dominated by the sounds of various machines: the high-pitched beep beep of the reversing loader, the diet feeder's rhythmical churning of the cattle's breakfast, the high revs of the straw blower as it unfurls its stringy golden carpet into the cattle sheds, the occasional cattle call or human voice, the whoosh of gusting wind or the rat-tat-tat of hail on a galvanised roof.

The machinery is used in the fields as well and, at certain times, such as when the weather improves after a poor spell, the countryside hums with tractors and other engine sounds while the screeching cries of gulls as they swoop to feast on worms in the freshly-turned sod momentarily stirs the senses to a saltier clime.

The fields are primarily the domain of the animals: the powerful jaws of the cows tearing off grass at the base, then lying down, regurgitating to chew their cud, swallowing and then getting up again, stretching and perhaps emitting an uninhibited fart or belch.

Horses tend to be more genteel in their personal habits – they even chew with their

Rain pounds down.

Limousin bull 'Clicker' bellows.

Ruth – Tears of a child.

terror. Then there is the cry of the vixen, as Sarah puts it, "wailing when she wants a partner."

Of all the farm sounds, none is sweeter than the clucking of the hen after laying an egg. It is loud and proud as she announces her achievement, and it is an amazing feat. As far back as Ancient Egypt the hen was feted as 'the bird that gives birth every day'.

We only recently got hens, primarily for their eggs but also in the hope that they would be pets. And they have delivered in spades on both fronts. We got a pair of Rhode Island Reds (Rua and Tallulah) and a pair of Sussex Crosses (Crystal and Gale), the last-named starting to lay within a week of arriving, to the girls' utter delight. These were later followed by a Speckled Marran (Speckles) and a Black Rock (Sweets).

mouths closed rather than open – and the language associated with them is more refined "whinny", "roll", "trot", "gallop"… though being kicked by one of them can elicit language from the recipient that is far from refined.

Growing crops make a range of generally delicate sounds, like the silky swish of growing silage grass or barley jingling as it ripens. While crops grow relatively slowly, they can disappear from the land very quickly and this changed environment presents challenges for the wild inhabitants. When silage has been cut and the ground is hard, Robin often hears a rabbit stamping his foot warning his family of an intruder.

Sometimes there are cries of distress: the cow whose calf becomes momentarily unsighted, the laboured uneven breathing of the heifer with pneumonia, the flurried scuffle of the fox pouncing on the rabbit followed by the latter's high-pitched, then quickly quenched, cry of

Rattling silage trailer.

Some experts advise that hens do not like much handling, but ours are regularly picked up, vigorously rubbed, dropped, chased and generally tormented. Despite this, they have continued to lay.

Sarah is a quiet child but she took to the hens straight away and wasn't at all put off by their flapping wings. She has spent countless hours with them, carrying them around wrapped up in her arms and talking to them the same as she would to any pet. Ruth, on the other hand, has had great fun teaching them to play "jump" (for food). It is hardly surprising that the hens sometimes get fed up with this robust kind of treatment and object with a peck, an event that often ends in tears.

Admittedly, hens produce a fair bit of poo and are not big into cuddling or playing ball. But they have been a most welcome addition to our farm life …and their delicious eggs a delightful supplement to our diet.

A harvest sunset.

Farm visitors

Hardly a day goes by without someone visiting the farm; we probably get several hundred visitors a year.

While friend or neighbours sometimes call for a chat (or maybe to borrow or lend something!) most visitors are people who provide a service related to the running of the farm. Some of these are profiled in the book but there are many others such as Roy Bailey (hedge-cutting and digger work), Eamon Meade (baling), David Thompson (plumber), Eamon McGarry (hoof care), Martin McDonald of Stradbally Town & Country (barley seeds and sprays), Mattie Kennedy of Liffey Mills and Michael Byrne of Portlaoise Veterinary Supplies.

In addition to Department of Agriculture, Food and the Marine or Bord Bia inspectors who come for regulatory reasons, we receive occasional visits from domestic and overseas meat industry representatives or broader agri-business representatives and live exporters. We also get the odd academic researcher or journalist… or, occasionally, someone looking to buy a site or a bale of straw.

The majority of our visitors, however, are groups of students (ours is a Teagasc benchmark farm used for student training) and farmer discussion groups. These would generally be given a tour of the farm, led by Robin, stopping at the various points of interest, the cattle and the sheds, particularly the 2005 shed (that Robin designed and which has been reproduced in various guises across the midlands).

"It's not for us to judge why farmers come here," Robin points out. "What I will say is that we have an open book policy. We don't bear a torch for anybody and, honestly, we tell it like it is for us, including the problems we encounter and how we deal with them. We emphasise that we are not saying that what we do is the right way to farm, rather it's what works for us.

"It is a nice feeling to think that people are interested in what you're doing," says Robin, and he particularly enjoys standing in the middle of a field of stock and being part of a discussion (sometimes heated!) about a topic such as suckler cow genetics or autumn versus spring calving.

Indeed, he points out that it can be an anti-climax if, for whatever reason, there hasn't been some debate about what is happening on the farm or what people perceive to be happening. In other words, if there isn't any feedback. In a variation of the well-known business motto, Robin feels very strongly that "if you see something you think we are doing wrong, tell us rather than talk about it on the bus on the way home."

We always try to facilitate anybody who wants to visit, even though, with the exception of the Teagasc student visits, we do not receive any remuneration for these visits. Having said that, overseas visitors often bring souvenir gifts ranging from Scotch whisky to French wine to Swiss chocolate.

"I am a great believer in the philosophy that if farming is to survive then farmers need to share their experience and information," says Robin, "and I would always welcome new research with an open mind. I would never be afraid to change, never be afraid to make a mistake… only try not to make the same one twice!"

Joe Kelly, who previously spend a student placement on the farm, returns with classmates from Kildalton College.

Agricultural Science Association visit farm, Brendan Barnes, Director Animal & Plant Health Association, Robin, Dr. Karina Pierce, President ASA & Lecturer UCD and Peter Bolger, of John Bolger & Sons, Agri Merchants, Ferns.

Robin speaks to Teagasc students.

Members of Laois Farmer Discussion Groups with Tom Everard on right.

Swedish researchers Cecilia Hagberg and Håkan Loxbo with Robert Leonard, Dept of Agriculture & Marine, Robin and Tom Ryan, Teagasc.

Pat Kelly completes Bord Bia inspection with Robin.

Robin with Paddy Murphy, Cork.

Robin chats to Mattie Kennedy, Liffey Mills.

Robin applies AluSpray to aid healing of skin after removal of horn bud.

Sarah – are we done yet?

Robin displays a calf's freshly removed horn bud.

Ruth plays in fresh barley straw.

Shane Phelan from Cullohill plasters inside wall of the grain store.

Padraic Murphy and Robin close the gates after the weanling bulls.

Cow licks her newborn calf.

A ripening head of spring barley.

A young calf enjoys his first rays of sunshine.

Leaves are already on the ground as the grain is coming in.

A Ruff and a Blacktailed Godwit visit.

August

Calving gets under way. This month and next are the most important months of the year.

Over the past few years we have been operating a night-feeding regime for the in-calf cows and this continues to work well, with most calvings occurring during the more sociable daylight hours.

Ruth advises Robin on stone picking.

Ruth – is that where you wanted this stone?

There is some good weather in late August and when I remark to Robin one day that at least the barley isn't lodged, he throws me his best 'easily-know-you-don't-come-from-tillage-country' look, explaining that this is because there's not enough weight in the heads of corn for them to be knocked over by rain.

The harvest begins.

Spring barley

By Robin Talbot

We sowed more barley in 2012 than we had done in a good number of years: a total of 80 acres, over50 acres of which was in the same place,

Ring-rolling the barley ground.

on Simon's Hill.

In 2011, after a particularly bad crop of maize that we had been growing as a source of forage, we had decided, luckily, not to grow another bad crop in 2012. Plenty of people are sowing maize successfully under plastic but we are reluctant to go down that route. We tried it twice but gave up because of the cost of the plastic and also because, after the crop is harvested, the land looks awful with bits of plastic scattered all around the place.

The obvious thing to do with the land that we had been growing maize on was to increase our acreage of spring barley. This would ensure an adequate supply of home-grown grain and, as we had also been buying a lot of straw for bedding, it would also make us self-sufficient on that front.

Barley has been grown in this country since Adam was a boy and it is a simple crop to grow.

The first thing we do, in the springtime, is to spread all the farmyard manure from the cattle sheds on the tillage ground. Then we plough it in.

By late March/early April, as soon as ground conditions are dry enough, we prepare the seed bed which, on our soil here, usually means we will roll the ploughed ground and go straight in with a one-pass corn sower, having spread some artificial fertiliser post-rolling/pre-sowing, based on soil test results.

The GPS on the tractor is very useful for this task because it enables us to spread the correct amount of manure without overlapping. The problem with overlapping is that it can result in the corn becoming very lush and then lodging later in the year after heavy rain or wind. This then provides an ideal starting point for birds to attack the crop, which they will do with absolute enthusiasm.

Clifford Roe sprays fungicide on the barley.

Combine harverster empties its load into trailer.

We tend to sow the seed at 112kg/ha. We will usually use a compound manure with Nitrogen (N), Phosphate (P) & Potassium (K) before sowing, referring to the soil analysis and also to the farmyard manure that was already applied. Later on when the corn is up, we will spread Nitrogen to bring the total N allocation up to approximately 250 units per ha.

We usually apply a herbicide as soon as the crop has emerged, on the basis that "the smaller the weeds, the lesser and cheaper the spray." We also apply a small amount of fungicide at this stage to try to keep the corn disease-free for as long as possible.

Aside from the fact that it's difficult to justify the cost of spraying barley twice with fungicide, we are conscious of taking a minimalist approach and therefore we use what I call the 'count-back' system when it comes to the main fungicide spraying.

If we assume that the crop will be ripe around 15 August and the plant will be ripening off for the previous three weeks (disease is not an issue in that period), this brings us back to 20 July and, assuming that a good spray will keep the plant healthy for at least a month, this brings the spraying date back to the first/second week of June. The aim is to keep the flag (top) leaf as green as we can for as long as we can.

Although I love livestock, one of the greatest pleasures for any farmer is to walk out through a field of clean, standing, ripening barley on a nice, sunny July evening and listen to it rustling in the breeze.

As with many activities in 2012, weather was an issue and it effectively came back to front. In March we were picking stones and preparing the seed bed in what would be ideal harvest conditions. When we were drawing-in the straw in August a major concern was trying to avoid carrying muck out onto the road!

Fortunately, luck was on our side when it came to the harvest itself, as we got a dry week. Moisture was 19.5%, which is not a problem when you are keeping the corn on the farm as most of the ways of preserving it actually work best when it is not too dry. To

Production line. Barley is loaded into hopper for rolling and treating with a preservative and then offloaded onto trailer.

sell it as a cash crop, moisture would need to be down around 16-17%, which in reality would require a couple more sunny days, something we don't often get.

The average yield was 2¼ tonne/acre, which is far from good but at least we were able to get it all and, for the year that was in it, we couldn't complain. The one mistake we did make was with the straw.

The weather had been so unsettled that as soon as it was dry enough to go in and harvest the barley we got the baler in behind it. We knew the straw was scarcely fit but feared we would get no better chance and baled up half of it straight away. We left the rest of it and it baled up lovely a few days later, but the first lot heated like mad.

The barley is fed to the suckler cows and fattening cattle. Initially, post-harvest, it was stored in the cattle sheds and, since we don't have a drying facility, we got in a contractor to roll and treat the grain with an additive to preserve it. The product we selected is called Maxammon.

The cost of treating the grain came close to €40/tonne but when you consider that the preservative also has the potential to increase the protein, which it did in our case by 2.2% up to 13.8%, this meant that we got by on silage and this grain right up to Christmas. This saved us buying around 10 tonnes of soya.

It's more feed produced within our control on the farm for our cattle, reducing our costs… and, with some of the grain having travelled as little as 500 metres from field to feeding trough, it would be considered a very good number indeed in terms of 'food miles'.

Farm safety

There is a joke in journalistic circles that the winner of a competition for the most unlikely headline was "Farmers Happy". This is a (light-hearted, I think) dig at the robust ability of farmers to stand up for themselves. In reality, the probable winner of this competition would be, and there is no humour whatsoever in this, "No Farm Deaths".

Fatal accident statistics are published by the Health and Safety Authority (HSA) at the end of every year. Sometimes farm deaths are up, sometimes they're down, but they always remain high relative to any other sector. In 2012, the figure was 21.

There are many reasons for farm deaths but to my mind the main ones are: farms are inherently dangerous places because they are home to large, powerful machines and similarly-built but unpredictable animals. Farms are family homes as well as workplaces and many visitors may be unaware of the dangers. Then, for the farmers themselves there is the issue of familiarity which can lead to complacency and even carelessness; the records duly show that the main causes of death are vehicles, machinery and livestock.

Deaths also involve members of the public, and a lot of age-vulnerable people: children and those aged over 65.

On top of all this, there is the element of chance. In September 2012, Nevin Spence, his brother Graham and their father Noel died in a farm accident in Co Down. They were poisoned by slurry gas while attempting to save a family dog. For weeks afterwards, wherever decent people gathered, conversation inevitably turned to this tragic event.

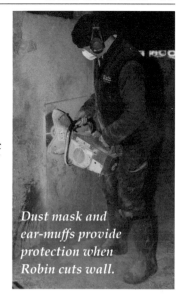

Dust mask and ear-muffs provide protection when Robin cuts wall.

Because our farm is close to the village, a concern for Robin is that someone visiting the village (he has no worries about the locals) and seeing a nice green field, might decide to hop over the gate to take their dog for a walk, not realising that they could be safer walking down the middle of the M50.

One of our few strict rules is that when there is a bull running with cows you don't go into the field without a vehicle. "You need to read the signs and heed the signs," says Robin. "If you have a stock bull and you think he's getting bad-tempered, the solution is not to be more careful handling him; it's to send him to the factory."

Robin is not convinced by the argument that a big problem for farmers, in terms of safety, is

Drive-shaft is covered to prevent accidents and replaced when showing signs of damage.

Calf tagging. Calf is separated from cow.

are just not utilised. However, he is reluctant to say much about this, recognising that he could easily become a statistic himself. "No-one knows when they themselves will make a bad call."

He does feel strongly that the often highly bureaucratic approach of the Health & Safety Authority is not helpful; neither is the Authority's suggestion of linking on-farm safety to cross-compliance inspections. More carrot is inevitably more successful than more stick.

"Farm safety is firstly a frame of mind. Get that right and the rest will follow."

the lack of time or money, pointing out that suitable handling facilities are often present but

Robin checks calf presentation with the safety of a calving gate.

Robin wears protective clothing when strimming.

A pair of cows at sunset.

Ruth in a white dress.

Robin applies splints to new-born calf with weak tendons.

Cows take to the new footbath with ease.

Students of Abbeyleix South School present a cheque to Bishop Michael Burrows.

Sarah does the herding on an early autumn evening.

Bishop Michael Burrows and Canon Patrick Harvey take to bikes as part of the former's Episcopal Vintage Peregrination around the Diocese.

Cow and calf share a tender moment.

Bill Meade bales straw in Ballygeehan.

Bumper crop on the pear tree.

September

There is a rural saying, often used in a bad year, that the stubbles get the best of the weather and this is exactly what happened this September. While some people feel the sunshine is too little too late, most consider it welcome anytime because it provides a much-needed, albeit temporary, lift to the spirits.

Robin finally gets around to building a footbath, in order to try to reduce lameness in the cows and improve their longevity. The end product is a simple, inexpensive construction and the cows take to it without complaint as they head outdoors every morning.

The harvest is completed, the barley treated and stored in a clamp.

Heifers, heifers, heifers

Once a calf is safely delivered, the first thing that many farmers do is lift their tail to check "bull or heifer". Beef farmers usually prefer to see a bull, dairy farmers are almost exclusively happier to see a heifer, each being more profitable in their respective sectors. Robin has never engaged in this practice, being satisfied enough that they are alive. But he is nearly getting tempted to do so because of a most curious pattern that has been emerging – over the last few years we have been birth a disproportionately high percentage of heifer calves.

While one occasionally gets a run of either sex, the pattern would usually even out over the season. In 2009, we had one more heifer than bulls, in 2010 we had two more bulls than heifers, so a pretty exact 50/50 split. But in 2011 we had 56% heifers and the trend became more exaggerated in 2012 with 63% heifers, a ratio of almost 2:1.

We did consider the possibility that this could be due to the impact of one particular bull, so we looked at the calves sired by Clicker and found that his pattern had changed in line with the overall pattern.

Quantitative geneticist with Teagasc Donagh Berry, for whom sex ratio is a pet academic hobby, points out that almost all species have a sex birthing ratio of 52% males, 48% female.

Young freshly calved cow and her calf.

But the ratio can be affected by a number of factors, including the weather conditions in a particular year, which he suggests could be the cause in our case.

Donagh has examined the factors associated with the sex birthing ratio of cows and he references a theory called the Trivers-Willard Hypothesis, which essentially says that cows in poorer condition are more likely to have females. He wondered whether our cows might have lost more condition in the run-up

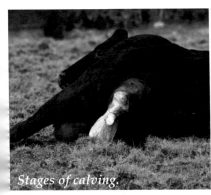

Stages of calving.

Cow needs assistance of a calving jack.

to the 2012 breeding season when compared with the previous year.

"The hypothesis comes from pre-domestication of animals when one male was the leader of the herd and would fight off all other potential leaders, so therefore had to be physically strong," says Donagh. "If a cow was in poor condition (either sick or with lack of access to ample nutrition), it was likely to have a weaker-than-average calf. Therefore, the best way for an individual [bull] to ensure that its genes would live on was to have a female calf

Nearly there. Calf is alert and ready to go.

since she would undoubtedly be mated."

While every herd might have a thin cow or two, most of ours would tend to be on the fleshy side. Indeed, Robin strongly believes that good body condition is imperative to the cow's ability to stay healthy herself and to raise a calf while quickly becoming in-calf again.

Body condition can affect fertility but the calving interval for our herd in 2012 was 372 days, which is somewhat better than the average of almost 400 days. This suggests that our cows are not thin, although it's possible they may be getting thinner.

Of course, if we could only work out what is happening and bottle it, we would make a fortune selling the secret to dairy farmers.

Rainy Weather

Death comes in many ways – unexpectedly, accidentally, slowly, quickly, painfully, peacefully – and many ports in between. Sometimes, someone makes a decision to end a life. I did this in 2012 for a thoroughbred mare. Her name was Rainy Weather. She was 33.

Horses are bred for pleasure and she certainly provided that. By Menelek, she was bred in Limerick by my uncle Joe Magner and she came to my mother Rita as a foal. She was broken by my brother Johnny before he moved to America and became a professional jockey. She was trained, under the watchful guidance of my mum, by my other brother Gerry.

Some (older!) point-to-point followers may remember the day she first appeared in Liscarroll, Co Cork, in March 1984 in the pouring rain and cantered home 20 lengths

clear in the hands of Gerry, who was just sixteen and having his first ride. It was a very proud day for my family.

She mightn't always have been the best but she always tried her best. She went on to win four more point-to-points, the last of which came in Buttevant where she looked set to

Happy 33rd birthday, Rainy Weather.

finish a clear second to PP Hogan's It's All Very Fine, only for him to tip up at the last and leave her to collect.

Afterwards, Enda Bolger (rider of the faller) gave my mother a slap on the back, saying, "Well done, Mrs, you needed it more than he (PP) did anyway". Rainy bred eight foals, the most successful of which was Tobeornotobe, which I raced for a while and which later earned some small black type.

While we obviously valued Rainy for what she achieved, she meant far more to us than that. Because she was around for so long she was an intrinsic part of our history. She was a link to my family, and to my childhood in Ardagh where I grew up. I was 15 when she was born and she lived through the untimely deaths of my brother Johnny and my mother as well as Rachel. Rainy was also with us for many happy events, of course, but the nature of the impending event – her own death –

Rainy, heading towards the light.

brought the sad memories to the surface.

It's not that I saw her as a person or as having comparable importance, but she gave my life a sense of continuity just by being there, a silent uncomplaining presence that I somehow interpreted as support. For that backing I felt particularly grateful and it made the decision to put her down all the more difficult.

She was also fairly likeable, with a really big bolshie spirit that could one minute knock you over with a swing of her big head and its skewed blaze, the next minute nuzzle into your arms for a good scratch of some hard-to-reach place.

When we had her put down, I cried for any happiness that she might miss out on and I cried for us – for the fact that she will no longer be part of our lives, that this cherished character is gone forever. A chain has been broken.

The fact that she was old doesn't mean I'll miss her any less. Her body might have worn out but her spirit remained bright to the end. What it does mean is that it should be easier to accept, as it is in keeping with the natural order of things.

I had known for some time that her death was approaching. I have to admit that I had been hoping nature would intervene and that I might go out to the field one day and find that her brave heart had just given out. It would have been a relief not to have had to face the decision that I eventually had to make.

For several years, Rainy had lived in one of three paddocks around the house so I would see her every day. Whenever I glanced at her casually from a distance, she appeared to be fine; she might prick up her ears or deeply exhale a sigh of pleasure.

Up close it was a different story. Her skin had become as dry as parchment and was stuck to her ribs, her eyes were sunken, her backbone protruding, her movements stiff. She still had a powerful walk and while her hooves needed to be dressed we were afraid to call the farrier because her balance had become very poor, as had her eyesight and hearing.

Only her big, plate-like hooves, which had once helped her gallop through the mud, remained unchanged. Once tipping 16hh, I never realised just how small she had become until Ruth, who is tiny herself, one day asked if she could rub my "pony".

I knew that having Rainy put down was the right decision, but that didn't make it any easier. I didn't know for sure that she was in pain but I could see that her body was shutting down. She had lost interest in food and spent a lot of time standing as if in a daze, alternately resting one leg and then another, so I do know that she no longer had a good quality of life. What she did still have was her dignity and I would have hated if something were to happen and cause her to lose this, such as running into something or falling and not being able to get up again.

As well as bringing back memories, facing that decision also prompted questions about the meaning of our own lives and mortality. It made me question my judgement and even my right to decide. Then I reminded myself that Rainy was my responsibility and that I had to make a decision in her best interest.

Rainy had a long life, a full life, a good life. None of us relishes the prospect of our own demise but I have to say that when my time comes I would have no complaints if the same could be said of me.

Seamus Moran, *large animal vet*

While the demise of the Celtic Tiger has devastated the Irish economy, it has also triggered a welcome injection of new blood and energy into Irish farming, raising the esteem in which the occupation is held. Every cloud has a silver lining.

"It's sexy again," smiles Rathdowney vet Seamus Moran. The seemingly interminable decline in the age profile of farmers has long been something of a hobby horse for Seamus and he thinks the revival is "great".

This is not because it has made any appreciable difference to his business. Demand for his skills remains virtually unchanged in recessionary times or boom times. Rather it has restored respect for an activity he has been involved with for 35 years and for which he has such high regard.

Seamus says that up to a few years ago if he had made a mental journey along any of the roads in his practice, it would have been very easy to count the number of lads (males and females) who were full-time farmers.

"People were almost ashamed to say they were farmers. It wasn't even that young people were being drawn away from the land; it was also the fact that the parents themselves were not encouraging their children to stay, as they felt it was not fair to do so given the opportunities elsewhere and the general lack of confidence in farming."

While 2012 will go down as a very difficult year for farming, Seamus feels that the sector has turned a corner following the influx of young people to carry it forward with new ideas and determination.

Seamus grew up on a small mixed farm near Templetuohy, just over the border in Co Tipperary. When he was doing his Leaving Cert he was thinking of becoming a doctor but he was put off by his teacher (there was no formal career guidance at the time) commenting that there was no background of medicine in the family. "Sure nobody in my family had ever even gone to university," Seamus now says wryly.

Instead, he starting studying agriculture in UCD with a view to specialising in his other love, horticulture — until one day he decided to switch to veterinary. Seamus is still not sure why he changed but out of the blue it just seemed the right thing to do and he has never regretted it. On qualifying in 1978 he got a job with Dan Delahunty in Rathdowney and has worked in this mixed practice ever since, taking it over on Dan's retirement four years ago.

Seamus says his job hasn't changed very much during all that time, although individual years vary somewhat. In 2012, for example, there was a lot of grass tetany very late in the year due to weather-related stress. He also performed a lot of caesarean sections in the spring, presumably because cattle prices were high at the time and calves were so valuable.

What gives him the most pleasure is the thrill he gets from diagnosing something unexpected. "You get the feeling that not many people can do this. Like agriculture, it is a really useful profession. You are accomplishing something."

The one thing he does not like is trying to collect money. "Some people are good payers, others are not, and this is the case regardless of how farming is doing. I would happily work all day every day, but the only reason I'll retire is because I don't like this aspect at all – the awful part of chasing money, the sense of insecurity it provokes and the fact that you always have to be doing it, to such an extent that the good is gone out of it by the time you get it." But Seamus is anxious not to place too much emphasis on this, as he enjoys dealing with most of his clients.

Indeed, he feels very privileged to enjoy such close relationships with so many people – relationships that go far beyond their cattle. If for example he is performing a caesarean section, which takes a couple of hours, the conversation will often range far and wide.

Even when Seamus was in college there was a lot of talk about how the role of the vet was going to change, how it would be moving away from the reactive, firefighting kind of work to focus more on preventive health plans for herds. Despite that, he says the former activity still accounts for 99% of their work.

Seamus believes that Bovine Viral Diarrhoea (BVD) testing, which became obligatory in 2013, will quickly lead to the eradication of the disease, though he is less hopeful about the elimination of TB. He points out that there are very few farms that don't have a badger sett and that not all badgers are infected. "The only way to get rid of it would be to test all badgers every year."

An animated Seamus Moran, centre, talks to Bosco Cowley, Technical Manager of MSD Animal Health while a worried Robin looks on.

Seamus Moran prepares an injection.

Robin and Seamus observe a sick bull.

Instant response. Padraic Murphy and Seamus Moran share a joke as a cow with grass tenany is administered calcium and magnesium intravenously.

Roy Wallace, *fencing contractor*

All land-based activities were hit by the wet weather in 2012, few worse than the work of people such as Roy Wallace, a fencing contractor from Mountrath who runs Wallace Fencing with his sons Derek and Trevor.

The early months of the year were good and there were hopes of a bit of a bounce but it quickly turned into "a disaster," says 29-year-old Derek. "Nobody would even think of getting a job priced when it's raining." Roy takes up the story, "You'd get away with a wet day in Ballacolla but not a month, and then if you scale that up to marginal land…" he trails off with a sigh.

Roy's father and grandfather farmed before him in Ringstown and he himself milked cows for many years, "when you could make a living out of 20,000 gallons". But as the bills got bigger and the money coming in didn't, he had to look at other options. At the time, eldest son Stephen was working for the Farm Relief Service and Roy went fencing with them himself for a number of years, "learning the business and the people", before striking out on his own about ten years ago.

During the Celtic Tiger years there was a lot of commercial work. Not only has all of that now dried up but Roy says there is also less demand from farmers. "They had to hire me or someone else when the sons were gone off to the building sites. Now the sons have come home and are available to do whatever work is needed on the farm." Turnover has halved from a high in 2006/07. One minor compensation is that it has resulted in more direct selling of stakes and similar items out of the yard.

Of the three types of farm fencing, Roy reckons barbed wire is "still the best for farm boundaries". He says that post and rail "is the hardest; because it is generally in a highly visible location and therefore it has to be 110 percent right", i.e. it should flow so that from a distance you should not be able to pick out the joints. Electric fencing is "the easiest to handle" but the downside is that there is a lot of walking involved. He estimates that for every 1,000 metres of fencing he would walk three times that distance.

Roy's favourite job is planning a fence. A couple of years ago a farmer who wanted to reorganise some land he had bought asked Roy to come up with a layout. "It took me nearly a day… working out which way to run the fields so as to be able to manage them best. It was a challenge, but very satisfying."

Usually, when on a job they remain on site for the day, breaking only to eat. When I ask whether it's difficult to work with family, Roy looks genuinely taken aback by the question. "That's a hard one, I've never thought about it," adding, after a moment's consideration, "too often, I suppose, a young lad is gone a hundred miles in the opposite direction" (too often, children choose to live and work far away from their family.

Roy Wallace.

Roy ensures post is straight before it is driven.

Derek Wallace.

Roy follows the unrolling wire.

Trevor Wallace with 'Sally'.

Padraic Murphy, *student*

If Padraic Murphy from Nuke, Co Wexford, is at all representative of Irish farmers of the future, then it augurs well for the survival of the sector and the strength of the social fabric of rural Ireland.

He came to us in August to study and work for three months. Sturdy of physique and personality, he was a positive and cheerful presence around the yard; willing to get stuck in, with the self-confidence to ask questions as well as to express his own opinion, not afraid to show manners or have a bit of craic. A welcome addition to the place.

At the time, he was in the process of completing his second and final year of the Drystock course at Kildalton Agricultural College in Co Kilkenny. One of the conditions of the course is that students must spend a period working on a farm. Placements are usually either in the spring or the autumn and the latter suits us best as it coincides with our busy calving/harvest period.

He grew up on a farm and his father Patrick (Paddy) is a well-known beef finisher who also runs an extensive cattle-dealing operation through a company called Knockbay Livestock. Padraic's long-term aim is to go home to farm, but he points out that his father is "still a young man".

Padraic has spent a couple of summers working in a beef processing factory and is already well on the way to developing an eye for judging stock. He has previously been offered some work buying cattle for a factory and says that, provided he passes all his exams, he might do a bit of travelling first. After that, he plans to do some factory procurement work while gradually taking on more responsibility at home.

The majority of those in his class come from a farming background and will end up farming at home, but he describes some of his classmates as "living in hope", believing, or at least thinking, that they may inherit from an uncle or other more distant relative.

Padraic believes that any young people going into farming these days are doing so because it's what they want to do and because they see a future in it, and he is very much of this mind himself. "Other sectors may come and go in terms of popularity but people are always going to need to be fed."

When asked what he learnt here, Padraic replies, "a totally new way of suckler farming, in terms of things like calving outdoors and ease of calving; and also the importance of measuring animal performance and keeping records."

During his time at our farm, Padraic stayed in digs with a local lady called Noreen Redmond and he often helped her out when he had finished his working day here – checking her cattle and doing a few jobs around the yard. She describes him as "having a great interest in everything; very grown up in ways but still with the best qualities of a boy."

Since leaving, Padraic has kept in touch with us and with Noreen. She has kept many lodgers over the years but didn't have to think too long before describing Padraic as "the nicest fella who has stayed here."

Padraic Murphy.

Padraic and Robin work on the new footbath.

Joe Hyland and Padraic Murphy.

Padraic waits on cattle to appear.

Padraic powerhoses the tractor.

Recipes

Buttermilk Scones

I am more of a fast cook than a good one, and I have a few simple recipes that I get by on. My favourite is Buttermilk Scones, which date back to my childhood. They are truly as light as air.

They require just six ingredients and after a bit of practice you probably won't need to use a weighing scales or even the recipe. You'll just need to remember the running order. Anyway, the measurements don't need to be exact. Scale up the volumes as required. Each ounce of flour will make approximately one decent scone. Without the sugar, they are delicious with soup or cheese and relish. Add 50g sultanas or currants for fruit scones.

If I know I am going to be in a rush in the morning I prepare everything the night before, up to the point of adding the liquid. Then I just have to turn on the oven, make the scones while it's heating and, within minutes, the rest of the house is waking to the uplifting aroma of baking bread.

Let them cool for a few minutes – if you're allowed to! As kids we used to grab them off the tray as soon as they were out of the oven, tossing them from hand to hand until they were cool enough and then wolfing them down. We were never, *ever* put off by our mum's warning: "Mind they don't stick to yer guts!"

Ingredients
225g plain or cream flour
¼ teaspoon salt
25g butter
¼ teaspoon bread soda
25g caster sugar
150ml buttermilk approx. to mix
Scone cutter or drinking glass.

Method
Heat oven to 200°C, Gas Mark 8.
Dust baking tray with flour.
Sieve the flour and salt into a large bowl.
Rub in the butter until it looks like breadcrumbs.
Spoon the bread soda into the palm of your hand and rub with your thumb to break up any lumps before adding to the mix.
Stir in the sugar, if you have decided to include it.
Add the buttermilk gradually, mixing with a fork to form a soft but not sticky dough. You may need less or more than the recipe states, so add it slowly.
Bring the dough together with your hands and turn it onto a floured surface.
Flatten it with your hand to about 1.5cm, depending on your preferred height of scone.
Stamp out the scones with a cutter or cut into wedges/squares with a knife and place on a baking tray.
Glaze the tops with a little buttermilk, if desired. A real cookbook would probably advise using egg wash, but I never have any to hand, and buttermilk works fine.
Pop in the oven for 10-15 minutes.
Cool on a wire tray.

Buttermilk scones with mixed red berry jam.

Mrs Nora Hyland's Red Berry jam.

Recipes

ACorN Cake

(Any Celebration or None).
This is basically a Victoria Sponge recipe which, by using Stork tub margarine instead of butter, can be whipped up by hand and into the tin at the speed of lightning. Definitely in keeping with my idea of low on hassle and high on taste.

This would make enough for a 20cm square tin or two large loaf tins. Quantities can easily be scaled up.

Ingredients
225g self-raising flour
225g caster sugar
225g tub margarine
4 eggs
1 tablespoon milk
2 teaspoon baking powder
This cake can be baked in whatever shape

you like and can be served plain any day of the week, or decorated and iced to produce something special for a celebration – hence the name Any Celebration or None.

I usually use this recipe for birthday cakes and, while it might seem a bit cheap to use margarine, it actually makes for a lighter, easier-to-eat cake when iced. Given that, with kids, appearance is more important than taste, it makes sense. Thankfully, the days when a bit of prudence and common sense were frowned upon are gone.

Method
I feel a bit pretentious even talking about method here, because there's so little to it.
Heat the oven to 170° degrees centigrade (10° lower if you have a fan oven).
Grease and line the baking tin.
Place all ingredients into a generous-sized bowl and mix with a spatula, only until smooth.
Pour the mixture into the baking tin, banking it well towards the rim.
Place in the middle of the oven for 20-30 minutes.
Turn onto a wire mesh to cool.
Lemon-flavoured cake is popular in this house, so I would finely grate some lemon rind into the mix. When the cake has cooled, add some lemon juice to glacé icing and pour over. When the icing has set, cut into chunks or wedges.

These are great for lunchboxes or when anyone drops in for a cuppa.

To make buns, just flavour the mixture with a teaspoon of vanilla extract.

For Valentine's Day, substitute 28g of flour with Bourneville cocoa, and bake in a heart-shaped tin. This tin is also suitable for making a cow's or pig's head!

Coffee cake with butter icing is Robin's favourite so, instead of the milk, I mix two teaspoons of coffee granules with one tablespoon of hot water and add this to the mix. For the butter icing, carefully heat 60g butter with one tablespoon of coffee granules and two tablespoons of milk at low heat in a microwave. When it has all melted, sift in 225g of icing sugar.

I often bake the coffee version in the loaf tins and when topped off with some chopped walnuts it makes an ideal contribution to the school cake sale.

War & Peace

A worldly friend tried to warn me but would I listen? "Surely at least you will build a separate kitchen?" she asked. "No," I said "it'll be fine". I was working full-time as an agricultural journalist and on the road a lot. I know they say that love is blind but nobody warned me that it could also be daft. I was marrying a farmer and going to set up home in my mother-in-law's house.

Since time immemorial, newly-wed farming wives have moved in with their spouse's family, joining parent/s and sometimes other relations. Especially nowadays and unlike other situations, this is not always or even primarily for financial reasons, more so practical ones.

This is going to be the family home sometime and the house is probably located on the farm so it is proximate to work; the parent/s may be advancing in age and need looking after. In Robin's case, his mum had been widowed at a relatively young age and he had always lived with her so she would have been lost without him.

The situation was changed by the arrival of our family. Before we married I would have intended to return to work if we had a baby but our first daughter tragically died and when we were blessed with the arrival of Sarah my priorities had changed and I became a stay-at-home mum so was around a lot more.

Conflicts started to arise and, while it is inappropriate to give specifics, what I can say is that there was never anything major, rather various small things. For example, we installed a dishwasher. There had never been one in the house before and Pam wasn't used to how it worked; my tendency would be to put it on once a day while she would tend to wash up after every meal. There is no right and wrong to this, just different approaches.

Of course if I had only thought back a few short years, I might have reconsidered our domestic arrangement. Shortly before my mother died, she had won a prize of a little silver ring dish with a horse standing on the outer rim and an inscription on the face. When she put it up in the hall, she turned the horse to the front. I was an adult living at home at the time and duly pointed out that this concealed the writing.

For ages after that, every time either of us passed it by we would turn it round the "right" way. It became a sort of a game between us. My mum and I were close but it just showed that two women in a home is one too many.

Moving in with the inlaws sometimes works; often it does not. Talking about this remains largely taboo but I know personally of situations where farm wives are treated

Ruth and Sarah behind Ann, Pam and Robin.

dreadfully by parents-in-law and siblings-in-law. Perhaps it is bitterness at the progressive tolls of time and declining physical power on the part of one and jealousy over inheritance by the other, or any of many other reasons, but it is often taken out on these women. They may become the trapped outsider, their marriage in tatters, suffering in silence or seeking escape in alcohol.

Check out any internet discussion board on the subject and you will be told that in-laws are the No 1 source of problems for newly-weds. Advice on living with them ranges from "No" to "God, No" to "Yes… if you want an early divorce."

Back to ourselves, I was becoming increasingly discontented and Robin and I spoke of moving out, to either rent locally or build nearby on the farm. While I always felt confident that our marriage came first I also recognise that he would have found it difficult as he loves his mother and no matter how near we were living I know he would have felt he was letting her down when she might most need him.

Pam did not want us to move. I spoke to her about this and, in fairness, she was very reasonable, asking what she needed to do to change the environment. She has always treated me with respect and showed a willingness to try to make things work. I said that to my mind neither of us was wrong, rather that the arrangement was not working.

She suggested signing the house over to Robin and me, if this would help. This was a very generous offer on her behalf but I rejected it immediately because I felt it could then make her the outsider, which I would never want. It could be her house or ours, not both.

Instead, we said we would like to convert the office into a kitchen and functionally divide up the house, which was big enough to facilitate this. That is what we did and, several years on, it is working quite well. We live largely separate lives from Pam but we do of course interact throughout the day and are close at hand if we are wanted.

It has taken a long time, effort and willingness to compromise to get to where we are now. We get on much better; we talk, argue, laugh. Yes, there are differences at times but we are now in a place where we can overcome whatever comes our way. It enriches our kids, too, to grow up with their grandmother around. Pam is in fine fettle and enjoying her retirement, which I now genuinely wish lasts for many more years.

The arrangement is not perfect, but then life rarely is and it's a long time since I recognised that everything does not need to be perfect in order to be happy. I would suggest that none of us is unhappy and everybody is getting much of what they want; me, more of our own space, Robin peace of mind and Pam company and security.

Had this compromise not been possible, all of our lives would assuredly be very different today.

Sarah (holding 'Teddikins'), Robin, Ruth (with 'Belle') and Ann.

Cows and young calves in the rain.

Cow and young calf.

Robin drives jeep through flooded yard.

Cow and two-month-old bull calf which is starting to muscle up.

Moorhen swims under rail outside front door.

Good as new, splints all gone.

First frost.

Water droplet hangs from ripening blackberry.

Robin with Leeson Stanley.

October

There is some lovely bright weather amid the appearance of the first ground frosts and morning fogs, which are common in these parts.

Calving comes to a close. It's been a very easy season; the calving jack is used so rarely that at one point Robin actually has to wipe cobwebs off it. Just one calf dies at birth, though a couple of "creaking doors" finally succumb.

We experience another deluge, with water pooling on parts of the land where we have never seen this happen. The land is saturated and cattle are housed a month early.

There isn't a single plum on a tree which this time last year was laden with fruit.

The pond in the Wild Place, home to much harvest merriment.

Wild plants come back into flower.

The Wild Place

All the decisions we make on this farm are in line with the best agricultural thinking and practice of the time. While most farmers have unknowingly done things that may have been detrimental to wildlife, one particular initiative of Robin's has certainly proved beneficial: long before it was fashionable he established a nature reserve.

There is a stretch of land to the north of the yard known as the Moor which had been tilled but which was always subject to waterlogging, even in dry years. In the early 1980s, Robin decided to tackle about five acres of this area and do something productive with it. He erected a sheepwire fence, then scooped out some of the soil in the middle and banked it all around to make an area to retain water; then he planted a wide band of assorted deciduous trees around the perimeter.

Now dubbed "the wild place" by the girls, it has been left untouched since and,

Male Bullfinch makes 'peu' call.

with the trees and vegetation now well grown, it has become their year-round adventure playground; perfect for recreating princess and fire-breathing dragon fairytales or playing hide-and-seek, with the leafy canopy offering a welcome oasis of cool during (rare) hot weather.

There is a substantial area in which bushes, flag irises, reeds and other wetland plants now flourish and this has become a haven for a range of wildlife, including small mammals such as foxes and rabbits, insects, as well as native birds such as Yellowhammer, Snipe, Bullfinch and Wren. In the yard we have seen a stoat which, presumably, comes from there.

The busiest area, though, is the pond. It usually, though not always, has water in it. During 2012, Laois County Council solved a longstanding flooding problem on the nearby road by installing a pipe connection to the pond, thereby increasing the water supply.

Some water-birds such as Moor Hen and

Little Egret. This Mediterranean bird is no longer a rarity in Ireland.

Mallard and her ducklings in the Wild Place.

Ann and Robin in the Wild Place.

Mallard breed here and live here year-round, but in winter it takes on another dimension as numbers swell many hundred times, thanks to an influx of migrant waterfowl: Shoveler, Teal, Mallard and possibly others that I don't recognise. It has also been acknowledged as a bird sanctuary by the local gun club and contains a release pen for Pheasant.

Outside the fenced area, significant areas of wetland remain and they attract large numbers of migrant waders which prefer open ground, mixed flocks of Lapwing and their relative, Golden Plover, as well as Curlew. We have also had the occasional Whimbrel, which is superficially similar to the Curlew but smaller.

The *Collins Complete Irish Wildlife* describes the Whimbrel as "a rather scarce passage migrant in spring and autumn, almost always on coasts and favours both rocky outcrops and sheltered estuaries. Winters in Africa."

We are always on the lookout for new arrivals. In September, we were chuffed to see the appearance of what turned out to be Ruffs and Bar-tailed Godwits, passage migrants and winter visitors from high Arctic breeding grounds. They are fairly commonly seen in Ireland but, again, mostly on estuaries and coastal grasslands.

We have also observed some Cormorants passing overhead. These are large, striking, black seabirds with a hook-tipped bill and they come inland in winter to feed on fish on estuaries and rivers. The Cormorants we photographed on our land spent this past winter based in tall evergreens near the Nore bridge on the R433 Abbeyleix to Rathdowney road.

So we can see – and often hear – literally thousands of birds from our back door for much of the year.

The Lapwing looks black-and-white from a distance but actually has an iridescent green sheen in sunlight and is easily identified by the stunning, curled feather that sits Mohawk-style atop its head. These occasionally breed here too, then you can hear their "pee-wit" cry which they are known by, warning off potential nest intruders.

Flocks often reach into their thousands, a remarkable sight in flight, sweeping steeply and banking back, round and round, time and again, their uneven wing beat making the group look like a highly dimpled, rather frayed, magic carpet rippling higher and higher, further and further away as they disappear into the heavens.

Formations of duck are even more spectacular as their brightly coloured bodies, which are surprisingly agile in the air, swoosh close overhead in tight formation like missiles. Robust in personality, they put on a pretty good show on water too, perhaps because of their looks and behaviour which are often associated with humour and silliness. Well, it is pretty nigh impossible not to look funny with your bum stuck up in the air while your head is feeding underwater.

When it comes to vocal performances, ducks are unequalled. The quintessential duck's quack we are all familiar with is actually the sound of the female Mallard and, if conditions are right, as on a clear harvest night when they are active and sound is travelling well, it is a life-affirming pleasure to step outdoors and soak up the uninhibited earthy atmosphere as their broad raucous banter rolls in like pub laughter across the moonlit air.

Top cow

The current top performer in the herd is Cow 49. *(See page 51).* Born on 17 April 2000 and purchased at Ennis Mart for €402 on 31 October 2001, weighing 294kg, she has a superb breeding record.

"She has always stood out from the herd… by her calf ." And that, to Robin, is the best way to judge a suckler cow – by what she is producing.

"In fact, she is never the first you would pick out on visual assessment; instead she is a prolific breeder who always has a good calf and does (feeds) them well. She has a good deep body, good pelvic width and, critically, is quiet."

However, Cow 49 will not retain her title of 'top cow' for much longer. Having produced her tenth calf in September 2012 she is now due for culling because of her age. Experience has taught Robin that no matter how good a cow is she should still be culled when her time comes.

Even if an older cow goes back in calf, she has a far greater likelihood of running into problems such as producing a dead calf or being unable to get up after a difficult calving. Farming is a business and sentiment does not cloud Robin's judgement.

The replacements

We cull up to 40 cows a year, for reasons including age, infertility, lameness, wildness or poor quality of calf. These are generally replaced by heifers bought through the marts. Our objective is to try to ensure that these replacements are genetically superior to those

being culled, but this is a huge challenge because that information is not yet readily available.

Given the considerable progress that has been made in Irish agriculture in the past 40 years, Robin finds it disappointing that "when farmers go to the mart to buy a heifer for breeding they are not being told even one more thing about her genetic merit than they ever were."

COW 49 BREEDING RECORD						
DOB	Sex	Weight (Kg)	Price (€)	Grade	Days on Farm	Daily Wt Gain
04/09/02	M	504	893	U3	364	1.275
06/09/03	F	440	746	R3	362	1.1
01/10/04	M	600	1271	E2	566	0.99
18/09/05	F	656	1213	U3	731	0.85
30/07/06	F	621	1357	E3	730	0.8
07/10/07	F	679	1192	U-3+	759	0.84
15/09/08	B	548	1041*	exported	373	1.36
10/08/09	F	388	912*	exported	355	0.98
06/08/10	F	726	1925	U+4-	622	1.11
08/08/11	M	560	1200*	exported	379	1.36
18/09/12	F					

*group average weight and price

The collection of information about commercial breeding has been under way in earnest since the establishment of the Irish Cattle Breeding Federation (ICBF) in 1997 and beef-breeding indices for individual animals are now being issued to farmers who have signed up to the ICBF Herd Plus information service. However, there is still no mechanism in place to make this information publicly available.

Robin would love to see some of the bigger marts and some of the breed societies coming together to run a couple of breeding sales a year where, in order to be eligible, a heifer would have to have a certain minimum index.

"Of course, the figures

in themselves are not the answer to all our woes. You still have to judge the animal on the ground. I would see them more like the headlights on a car that could point us in the right direction.

"When you first see a heifer, you really have no idea how she will work out. The reality is that 10 percent might turn out to be in the top tier of the herd, 70 percent may make good commercial cows, and the remaining 20 percent would fall below the required standard and would end up being culled sooner rather than later."

Breeding heifers in Tentore. Who will make the grade?

NOVEMBER

Calves step through the creep gate.

Buckthorn berries in Loughabarra.

Calves eat creep feed.

Sarah in a white hat.

Cow No 49 with her two-month-old heifer calf.

Adam Saldatsenka (right), a farmer from Belarus and his nephew Valery Vaniukevich (second left), Robin and Padraig Blake, Co Longford on behalf of livestock company Buitelaar Intl.

Silage bales and beech trees frame the original back gate of the former Ballacolla House.

Cow and pair of calves (not twins!)

Teal swim in Loughabarra.

November

Here we are thinking the weather is bad… until it really turns to winter. Although there are some delicious moments of sunshine, which we devour, the month is generally wet and dark.

Farmers are housing cattle at the same time that they are still trying to cut silage. Already there are prayers for an early spring.

The feeding and bedding routine is well re-established.

However, all the bad weather continues to cause problems. The silage and straw are both poor and the calves are neither thriving nor happy, so we call out the vet and send the forage off to be analysed.

The wet year

Nobody talks about the weather like the Irish. It's almost as if we don't realise that weather is an important factor in other countries too and that they also get bad weather, sometimes even more of it and more extreme than us.

What makes it different in Ireland, of course, is its unpredictability, which is the only consistent thing about it. In another country you could plan to go to the beach on Friday; in Ireland you would say you'd hope to get there some day in July.

It's not only the frequency with which we talk about the weather, it's also the language we use. "It's roasting" or "it's bitterly cold out there" suggests that at some primeval level we still feel it controls our behaviour. Perhaps it's because a lot of us are no more than a couple of generations away from the land where, despite all the technological advances, nature still rules.

We also have a narrow range of comfort, "a nice fresh day" being just a degree or two above "bloody freezing". Nowhere is our national pessimism more rampant than when it comes to the weather, so a conversation in the local shop that opens with "they're talking about the high twenties today" will inevitably end with "it's not to last, though."

And what is it, anyway, about unseasonably bad weather that we just can't handle?

In March 2012, when there was a burst of sunshine we had no problem swopping winter woollies for t-shirts, sunglasses and swimsuits. But when the wind and rain returned, we resisted putting back on the extra layers as if doing so would somehow ward off the reality.

It's easy for us to adjust our dress mode to deal with different weather conditions… unlike the poor animals which, having cast off their winter coats, must do without them until they grow back again and, in inclement conditions, they have to seek alternative protection. As for the plants, once they have poked out their pretty little heads they can't even go to look for shelter.

2012 had to be the ultimate topsy-turvy year in terms of weather. It was only marginally colder than average but that masks the fact that the first three months and August were milder while the other months were cooler. Much to the girls' disappointment there wasn't a single flurry of snow, but there was rain, lots of it and often at the wrong times, with June being its wettest ever almost everywhere. Sunshine is welcome at any time; the problem was we just didn't get enough of it, with most weather stations reporting the dullest weather in 7-18 years.

Hopefully, 2012 will continue to be remembered as 'the wet year' and will not prove to be a portent of things to come.

Floods rise to previously unseen levels.

Cattle Sales

By Robin Talbot

Our farm yields some 80 tonnes of beef a year – roughly equivalent to the amount of beef consumed by the entire population of Co Laois in a month. Another way of looking at it is that the total amount of beef consumed over the three days of "The Ploughing" is 15 tonnes.

We try to produce what the market tells us the consumer wants: young beef, reasonably lean, produced to the highest welfare standards in an environmentally friendly way. When cattle are being loaded to go for export or slaughter, it's neither a time for tears nor rejoicing, it's what we do.

It's a well-known fact that animals perform best when they are happy and contented each and every day and this is an important factor in getting them to their optimum weight at a young age.

In 2012 we sold a total of 222 cattle, the majority as beef to the local beef factory, Meadow Meats in Rathdowney, with some of the young bulls being sold live as weanlings. The performance of our animals is the culmination of our breeding and feeding programmes. While their main purpose is obviously to generate income, their performance also provides an evaluation of our year's work.

Sale prices were at record high levels in 2012, which was just as well because inputs such as concentrate feed and fertiliser were also at record high prices. We feel that we do this job reasonably well, but the farm could not operate as it currently does without a significant Single Farm Payment.

Irish beef cattle have traditionally been sold on a 'flat rate' basis but at the end of 2009 a new Quality Payment Scheme (QPS), which gives bonuses for carcases that meet market demand, was introduced and this has significantly improved the price we are paid.

This new scheme is based on the European EUROP classification system which classifies or grades carcases according to their muscularity and fat cover, giving an indication of the amount of meat that can be sold. E-grade cattle are 'Very muscled' while P-grade cattle are 'Lightly muscled'. Fat Cover 1 means 'Very thin' and Fat Cover 5 means 'Very fat'. The QPS is applied to the pricing of heifers and bullocks and we would *love* to see it extended to young bulls.

The QPS comprises 60 individual combinations of carcase grade and fat score and our target is to get as many heifers as possible to grade from R+ upwards. The right diet can aid this process but it's a very simple yet irrefutable truth that you can't get out of them what they don't have in them in terms of genetics. The ideal fat score is 3 to 4 and there are, rightly, heavy price discounts for very fat carcases.

Heifers are sold before they reach the age of two and sales of a particular generation would commence in the spring from the age of 20 months upwards. Those being targeted for sale at that time are identified at the start of the winter and they are fed a diet consisting of home-grown barley molasses and first-cut silage. We would expect these heifers to be gaining in the region of 1kg liveweight per day on this feed. This growing diet sets them up nicely to respond to their finishing diet, which includes a lot of home-grown grain. The finishing diet is fed to them for the last 80-90 days before they are sold. On this diet we would be hoping for them to gain at least 1.4kg/day.

Heifers, when they get to a certain point of maturity, finish very quickly so at this stage it's important to monitor them carefully to ensure that they don't get too fat. Consequently, we would start drafting (selecting) for sale on a weekly basis. Average carcase weight in 2012 was 335kg and kill-out percentage (how much of the animal's liveweight is utilisable) was 58%. Obviously, the higher this figure is the better, for both us and for the meat factory, as it means there is less waste on the carcase.

The average price achieved across all stock (including cows) was €1,477. Prices per head ranged from €1,181.14 paid for a heifer that spent 637 days on the farm, graded R+2+ and weighed 492kg with a kill-out of 56.89% which produced a carcase of 279.89kg, to €2,137.36 paid for a bull that spent 660 days on the farm, graded E-3 and weighed 776.56kg with a kill-out of 64% and a carcase of 497kg.

Any heifers, usually the younger ones, who are not going to be ready to be sold out of the

Peter Quinn of Meadow Meats with U+4- heifer carcase weighing 436kg, progeny of Cow 49.

Loading weanling bulls, heading to Northern Ireland for finishing.

Robin loads heifers going to meat factory.

Some of our bull carcases hang in the cold store.

2012 heifer progeny of Top Cow 49.

shed in the spring are let out to graze and they are then sold off grass over the summer. Bulls, by their nature, tend to mature at a slightly older age and thus at heavier weights. They also have a few percent better kill-out rates, around 60%.

One of the big talking points at our discussion group's October get-together was how best to optimise returns rather than maximising performance. This may sound obvious but there was a consensus that we need to get over the competitive issue of who has the best in terms of conformation and/or heaviest animals; farmers are proud of what they produce and tend to have an innate feeling that the heaviest animal is best even though they may not actually yield the most profit. The lighter, younger animals are more marketable and in addition the accepted view is that once the final push is completed – 90 days for heifers, 120-130 days for bulls – their feed-conversion efficiency starts to tail off.

The other large group of sales was of the weanling bulls aged just over 12 months. In the past, these have often gone to Italy for finishing but this year they went to Northern Ireland. These should be a prime product but it has become increasingly difficult to sell them because the pool of buyers is small. For the future, we are considering building another shed so that we are able to finish them ourselves.

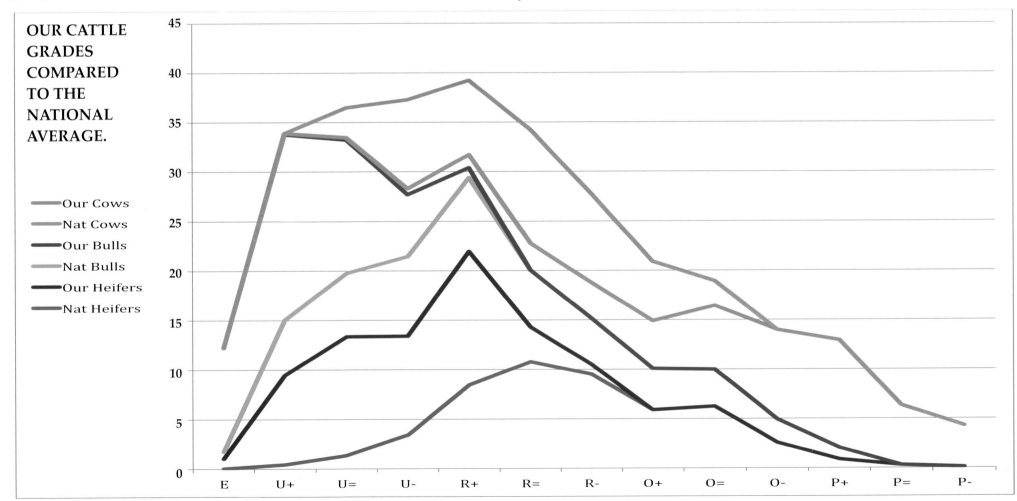

OUR CATTLE GRADES COMPARED TO THE NATIONAL AVERAGE.

Our Cows
Nat Cows
Our Bulls
Nat Bulls
Our Heifers
Nat Heifers

Horses turn their back to one of the many heavy showers which characterised the year.

DECEMBER

Lethargic calves, subsequently diagnosed with IBR.

Our five hens, 'Gale, Rua, Tallulah, Speckles and Sweets'.

A Lapwing.

Cormorants perched high over the River Nore.

Mallards walk on the frozen pond in the Wild Place.

Fairytale atmosphere. House in fog days before Christmas.

Beef heifers in the yard for weighing.

A flock of Lapwing and Golden Plover.

Mid-winter celestial spectacle.

A robin.

Whooper swan family.

Joe Hyland removes tyres from the silage clamp.

Gwen Shirley spreads poultry manure when planting new hedge.

December

On the shortest day of the year, we are treated to a truly celestial sight: a thin fog blanket which drifts cold over us suddenly unrolls back across the sky like marshmallow cotton wool, settles on the horizon, then vanishes in an instant.

The forage test results finally arrive but are inconclusive. Though the crisis in the calves abates there is still a lot of malaise about.

However, Robin is good at parking his worries and we enjoy Christmas.

He weighs the fattening heifers and is pleasantly surprised to discover that they have been gaining an average of 1.2kg/head on their pre-final-phase diet.

2012 ends on an optimistic note.

Superman

Can there be a skill that a farmer is not called upon to turn his hand to?

Yes, but not many.

He (or she!) needs to be an agronomist, animal nutritionist, labourer, bookkeeper, the boss, materials scientist, machinery operator, mechanic, inventor, crisis manager and long-term planner.

He needs to know what short-term jobs to complete in order to achieve the medium-term goals that make up the long-term plan.

He must also be able to change direction in mid-stream, whether on his tractor or in his brain.

Do I sow corn or buy cattle, milk cows or sheep, go organic or intensive?

And he can't call in sick because he probably works alone.

He has to be able to read the signs of the weather and the economy, to talk to the shyster and the bank manager, to recognise opportunities and threats… and to know which is which.

No matter what advice he gets, he has to make up his own mind and live with the consequences – reap the rewards or pay the price.

The good decisions are rapidly subsumed into the whole. A bad decision can cost him a week's wages; a worse one, his business; and a wrong decision can cost him his life, or someone else's.

When an animal is poorly, does it need a bottle of medicine or a visit from the vet? He needs to know when to help the calving cow and when to simply wait; when to hold his beef cattle and when to sell them; when it is safe to go into the field and when the sensible thing to do is run.

Working in environments that are often beautiful and equally often harsh, he has to be brave and tough, occasionally gentle and, even less occasionally, still, so that he can listen to his own voice and to the telling sounds of the land.

An early bird and a midnight owl, he has to be patient and resilient; to use some clichés, he must make hay when the sun shines and save the pennies for a rainy day.

And, behind it all, just in order to survive, he must have a fully functioning sense of humour.

Why do they do it? Is it because they inherited the land or because they know nothing else? Or is it something they have always wanted to do, driven by a hunger in the heart?

And they are eternally grateful for the chance to work outdoors in the living world… the independence, the unique identity, the possibilities, the unpredictability of it all.

None of this wins any medals or delivers any bonuses… although it might earn the (usually unspoken) respect of his peers. And what greater accolade could there be?

More than that, if he's good at it and enjoys it, the sense of satisfaction and achievement it brings is incomparable.

A farmer might regard his professional sibling with awe, not realising that he himself is every bit as skilled. The only difference is that while professionals tend to specialise in one particular area, a farmer has to be a generalist.

Most of us can do one thing well, but to do so many things so competently truly takes a superman.

Superman he might be, but instead of a slick hairstyle, freshly manicured hands, a glamorous flowing cape and sheer tights, this superman is more likely to be sporting dirty fingernails, wrinkled hands and a weathered face, wearing an ensemble of beanie and overalls, bottomed off with moo-poo-spattered wellies.

Luckily, for those who live with them, most farmers know that the time to shower and shave is after work rather than before. As for the biceps… yes, they are invariably bulging and they are equally likely to be streaked with their very own oft-teased tan.

These supermen (and women) are everywhere. They are the quiet heroes of the land.

Love/Hate

By Robin Talbot

For as long as I can remember I have always wanted to farm. In 1973, when Ireland joined the European Economic Community (EEC, as it was then), I was just starting out in farming and I vividly remember the sense of elation and hope I felt at the possibilities raised by Ireland's membership. In addition to facilitating free trade between member states, the objectives of the EEC included improving agricultural productivity so that consumers would have a stable supply of affordable food and farmers could make a reasonable living. It had all the hallmarks of a recipe for success, with the two buzz words being intensification and mechanisation.

At the time, we were doing tillage, rearing sheep and buying store cattle in the marts, grazing them for a season and then fattening them in the sheds for sale in the spring. However, a turning point came for us in the late 1980s when hormones were made illegal. We continued doing stores for another year before it became apparent to me that not everyone was yet taking the ban as seriously as we were. We had always been able to compete at the ringside with other buyers for the cattle that we wanted but we found we were no longer able to do so. We had to implement a major change.

Starting off with about 30 heifers of different breeds, we let a Hereford bull out with them. We subsequently bought suckler cow quota every year and this practice has formed the basis for today's herd of 220 cows.

Cattle shed built in 2005 with EU grant aid.

We have always embraced the Common Agricultural Policy (CAP), adopting any relevant schemes as they came on stream and maximising their contribution to the farm. Therefore, when farming support moved to an area-based system we were able to qualify for a substantial Single Farm Payment (SFP).

Every sector of agriculture has benefitted enormously from European Union (EU) membership. The Irish countryside today is dotted with modern, tasteful livestock housing and has a generally prosperous air. As did most other farmers who had the financial resources to do so, we continuously improved farm infrastructure, ploughing our profits back into the business. I am hugely grateful for all the financial support we have received.

However, the CAP has not been an unqualified success and the relationship is not always an easy one… a bit like the relationship you might have with an interfering mother-in-law; trying at times, but also beneficial – without her you wouldn't have your lovely wife.

In my view, the core problem with the CAP has been the failure to craft a long-term vision. One day we are encouraged to increase production, the next day to decrease it. In relation to the Nitrates Directive, something which was deemed to be good farming practice on Monday had, by Wednesday, made us liable for a penalty on our SFP.

The policy has been reformed a number of times and each modification brings a different

vision and is couched in different language. For example, the SBP (Special Beef Premium) was supplanted by the SFP. As I write, we are in the midst of the latest round of reforms and there are undoubtedly plenty more letters to come out of that particular hat (or at least CAP!).

If the SFP is substantially diluted, the lights in rural Ireland will start to dim and the impact may be felt most by the people with whom we do business. While we are self-sufficient in terms of stock to sell, we may end up producing fewer animals and spending less on them.

There are interesting times ahead, no doubt!

Noel Bailey, *contractor*

Contractor Noel Bailey from Grantstown is many different men bound up in one. He is a tough, hardworking businessman, a family man with a soft spot for animals, and an ill man with a deteriorating physical condition. But perhaps his defining persona is that of a positive man.

It is the ill man that I feel anxious about interviewing because I don't know how he is coping, but he is immediately forthcoming and frank. "Talking is how I deal with it. I will blather to anyone and everyone."

Noel first noticed that something was wrong in 2007 when he was 53 years of age. He was writing a Christmas card and, although he has always had a good "hand", he noticed that the pen was not writing smoothly. There followed many trips to experts in various fields and the current medical opinion is that he has multiple sclerosis (MS) from the head to the hips and Motor Neurone Disease (MND) from there down. Whatever about the label, the result is that he is experiencing increasing paralysis on the right-hand side of his body.

Either of these conditions on its own would be frightening but, while his wife Ann, son Darren and daughter Saphron have been "gutted" by the diagnosis, Noel says that he himself is not. "No, really, I'm not just putting on a front," he says with conviction. Noel is "positive that MND or MS will not kill me. Yes, they will shorten my years but I feel I will live a full life and die of natural causes."

His candour and courage are humbling and inspiring.

Noel recognises that he is now struggling to operate machinery and that the time may come when, for health and safety reasons if not for others, he may have to give up contracting, a business he first got the taste for when working with local contractor Richard Moynan (RIP April 2013) to help pay his way through college.

I have heard from a reliable source that Noel was a brilliant student and he confirms without fuss that he achieved good results in his higher diploma in industrial engineering at Carlow Regional Technical College (now the Institute of Technology, Carlow). He was offered plenty of jobs but didn't take any of them because of his "love for the land".

His father Dick had a tractor and Noel started doing a bit of contracting himself. There was no great defining moment when he decided that this was what he was going to do but in 1975 he bought a new 100hp Ford tractor for £4,750 (the exact amount slips off his tongue), two new silage trailers for £1,100 each and a double-chop silage harvester for £2,000. He duly went on to become the best in the business.

Noel had inherited the 80-acre family farm and he rented a lot of land for sugar beet, but the demise of that industry was followed by the onset of his illness. Today, he still does tillage and silage but says that rising fuel costs are crippling.

"For ten years I changed the forage harvester every year but now I don't think I ever will again. Darren might but I won't." As for the future of the business, they have taken up wood chipping for heating commercial premises and are looking at other opportunities such as using willow for heating.

"The business was part of me but I will have to take a side-seat [he refuses to say back-seat] reluctantly. I find the idea of that difficult as I have always been a hands-on person. I covered silage pits for over 25 years and it annoys me that I no longer can…", his voice trails off.

But he is quickly positive again and points out that as well as drystock the farm is now home to a variety of animals including donkeys and a couple of shire horses, "purely a hobby", that are central to Noel's other interest – running a live crib, which he has done for a number of years and which raises a lot of money for local charity.

"It's not from out of any great holiness, more that I have an interest in the old traditional stuff. The animals also go to other events which showcase associated skills like hot-shoeing and haymaking… just for the flute (hoot) of it," he laughs.

Looking to his personal future, Noel can see himself "sitting in my free, disabled-access bedroom, which was provided by Laois County Council without any fuss, working a computer, maybe giving advice about machinery, farming or health problems."

As to what he would like to be remembered for (some time in the far-off future, he hopes), Noel is quiet for a moment and then flashes a look of bright determination. "For being straight up, for trying my best."

Noel picks up silage under an ominous sky.

Noel rolls the tillage ground.

Hughie Dunne, Borris-in-Ossory ploughs for Noel Bailey.

Noel Bailey.

Tom Everard, *Teagasc adviser*

Teagasc adviser Tom Everard could retire (on a full pension) any day, as he's "gone the sixty", but providing his health holds and clients continue to want him he intends to continue working up to the obligatory retirement age of 65… because he likes dealing with people and gets great satisfaction from helping them. What a wholesome attitude to work and life!

The second eldest of twelve children, Tom was raised on a 110-acre mixed farm near Templetuohy, Co Tipperary, where the influence of agricultural advisers fuelled his own interest in the area. Shortly after getting his Agricultural Science degree from UCD in 1973, he landed, with the help of the late Lar Broderick from Ballacolla, a job as agricultural adviser with the County Committee of Agriculture, the precursor of An Chomhairle Oiliúna Talmhaíochta (ACOT) and, subsequently, Teagasc.

Tom is a drystock adviser, with a client list of 200, including ourselves.

One of the main ways he assists clients is in helping them to complete the complex paperwork to apply for schemes such as the SFP. In many instances, advisers such as Tom are the interface between the farmers and the bureaucratic system, and he believes it is wrong that drystock farmers in particular, who depend so heavily on such payments, are living in fear of making a small mistake that could jeopardise their receipt of these payments.

Tom also has a development role through the Beef Technology Adoption Programme (BTAP) which involves assisting discussion groups, organising seminars and student education. In the context of the student education programme he is a regular visitor to this farm.

For the past number of years he was accompanied on these visits by Teagasc Environment/Technology colleague Lily Nolan, who sadly lost her long battle with cancer in November 2012. At the mention of her name, Tom, who up to this point in our conversation about himself and his career has been quite reticent, suddenly becomes animated, describing Lily's contribution to various programmes in Teagasc as outstanding, and her energy and positive outlook as inspiring.

Apart from a brief spell with the Department of Agriculture working on economic forecasting ("it was very high-brow stuff"), Tom has spent his whole career as an agricultural adviser and, despite the many changes in Teagasc, not least the reduction in staff in recent years from 1,500 to 1,000 as a

Tom and Robin lead a group of students on farm walk.

result of the embargo on recruitment, he feels very privileged.

"Of course, the first thing we whinge about is the increased workload but, honestly, morale is ok," says Tom. "I am always saying to my colleagues that it's the best job in the country; in the office in the morning and then out on farms in the afternoon, dealing with nice people for the most part. There is huge variety in the work. No two problems are the same. Well, actually," he checks himself, "sometimes problems are the same but no two individuals are the same."

Despite the many challenges facing the agricultural sector, Tom remains positive. "Farmers are very resilient. They battle through the hard and appreciate the good." As we say our goodbyes, he is heading off to see another client.

A group of Welsh students visit the farm with Tom Everard.

Tom Everard equipped with plate metre.

Tom shares as joke with Brendan Barnes, Director General of the Animal & Plant Health Association (APHA), Robin and Eamonn O'Reilly, Agri Advisor with AIB.

Tom with Teagasc colleague Lily Nolan (RIP) and Robin.

Ray Galbraith, *mechanic*

The more mechanised farms become, the more farmers depend on machinery. I know that's stating the obvious but the corollary is that a mechanical breakdown is a big deal and the security of having Ray Galbraith from Castlefleming as our mechanic is fantastic. No matter the day or the hour, Ray will always answer the mobile and say, "Sure, we'll get you going anyway."

Ray set out to train as a metalwork teacher in the National Institute for Higher Education (NIHE) in Limerick (now the University of Limerick or UL) but it didn't work out. Then in 1983, "kinda out of nowhere," he decided to do an apprenticeship as a mechanic with AnCO.

After qualifying, Ray went to work for Condells in Portlaoise. "I was earning sixty pounds a week, half of which was going on petrol, and it didn't take long to realise that there must be something more." So in 1986 Ray set up on his own, travelling around to farmers' yards "with just my toolbox and what I had in my head".

Ray's mum, Winnie, was the only teacher in Castlefleming National School and they lived in the house alongside. In 1974 the school was amalgamated with another school and his parents bought the building. Ray built his first shed in 1987 at the rear of the building. "Year on year, I worked hard, building up the business."

Of the many changes that Ray has seen in his 30 years as a mechanic, none has been greater than farmers' ever-increasing paucity of time.

Ray Galbraith.

"When a man is in trouble, he wants help there and then. It's no longer a case of, 'When can you come to me?', because tomorrow won't do."

This time pressure is reflected in the increasing size and capacity of machinery, which can get through a lot of work in a short space of time. "In the '70s the Massey Ferguson 188 (75hp) was a weapon; now it would scarcely be considered fit to draw diesel to the big combines, with 100-120hp being the norm for a farmer's tractor and contractors using up to 180hp." Likewise, most medium- to high-end tractors today have a series of electronic systems which control the engine, transmission, hydraulics and so on, requiring less physical effort on the part of the operators and enabling them to work longer hours.

Ray describes his job as "nearly seven days a week and not restricted to nine to six; you still have to do the paperwork. But I'm happy to work for myself. If you want to do something you don't have to ask anyone's permission."

He has a mini-digger which he will go off to do some work with when he needs a break from the garage. A hands-on family man, his other outlet is the "totally different" world of amateur dramatics.

Like many people, including a number of those profiled within these covers, Ray's greatest satisfaction comes from solving a difficult problem. "You could lose a bit of time on something but at the end there is a sense of achievement completely unrelated to what you're paid. I've said it all through the years: not a day goes by that you don't learn something new."

Mechanic, Ray Galbraith repairs the loader.

'Hodgepodge House', *Happy Birthday*

I've heard the house in which we live described as "the Big House" and, in terms of square footage it is pretty substantial, about 350 square metres (though it probably isn't as big as it looks as it is long and narrow). Like many farmhouses, however, it is actually an amalgam of old and new, with new bits added as needed or as could be afforded, so the overall effect is fairly hodgepodge.

The layout could certainly not be described as optimum and, while there are high ceilings and some fine old furniture, we have unashamedly introduced some cheaper, modern items that work well with a young family. The house is in reasonable condition, having been re-roofed a couple of years ago, and we generally try to keep it looking well both inside and outside.

Most of the current dwelling was built in 1912/13 (hence the 100th birthday wishes!) close to the previous thatched dwelling. Just before Peter's second son, Bob, married Pamela Jackson, a new kitchen extension was built, joining the newer house to a section of the old house, as it was also home to Bob's unmarried aunt Frances Talbot and his uncle Jack Tomlinson. (Bob's eldest brother Bill, an engineer, had already emigrated to South Africa to join their uncle, Benjamin, who was also an engineer.)

This extension was brought up to the second level in order to provide the house with a bathroom for the first time. Our kids find it hard to understand the notion of a house having no bathroom. Their school is very good at promoting the philosophy of maximising energy utilisation and the girls seem to think that this is a recent phenomenon. What they don't realise is that it is wastefulness that is modern. Today, the disposal of human waste is a costly and arduous process, but 100 years ago every bit of energy possible was utilised. Pam clearly remembers that, when she used to visit the house before her marriage, the human waste was emptied at the base of a particular plum tree (now gone!) which used to be laden with a bumper crop of fruit every year.

Pam continues to live in the house, and when Robin and I got married we built on a further two-storey extension to the back.

The house faces south and is situated below Simon's Hill across the road, well above yard level, which is effectively the base of the hill. Its orientation and position provide a certain amount of natural shelter from the elements and also mean that both the house and the farmstead nestle into, rather than impose themselves, on the landscape, the desirability of which from an aesthetic point of view is again getting greater recognition in our more subdued post-Celtic Tiger economic climate.

Dwelling house as it is today.

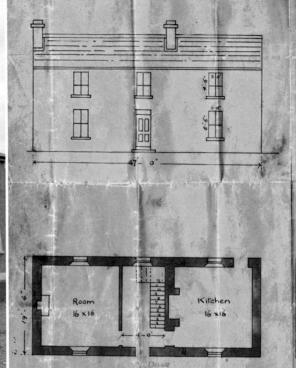
Plans for 1912/13 house.

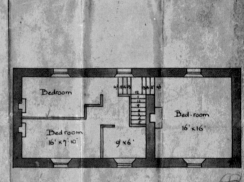

Peter and Harriet Talbot with baby William (Bill) in front of house, built in 1912/13.

Sarah's bedroom. A mix of old and new.

Recipe

Linseed cough mixture

Linseed was in widespread use up to relatively recent times, with one magazine from the 1950s containing an "Unfailing Recipe for Constipation" and I found the following "Good Cough Mixture" recipe tucked away in a shoebox in the storeroom. It was handwritten, possibly by Sis (Robin's gran-aunt Frances) on a well-spattered card.

Half a pint of fresh linseed from a good chemist.

Put a large teacupful in a saucepan and two penny worth of Spanish liquorice stick, four ounces of muscatels stripped from their stalks and two quarts of cold water.

Simmer very slowly until the bulk of the liquid is reduced to one half.

Then add four ounces of Demerara, a teaspoonful of rum, and the same quantity of lemon juice which should be added to each half pint of mixture before it is to be taken.

Just before bedtime a large draught will work wonders. During the day a little should be sipped whenever the cough is troublesome.

The recipe concludes: This remedy is said to be one of the finest that can be made.

According to a fascinating school-textbook-cum-farmer's-handbook entitled *Agricultural Class Book*, linseed jelly was an excellent food for calves and this 1881 book also advises "the first great means of affecting… an increase in income from livestock… is to diffuse among the people correct notions on the subject of breeding."

Something that remains good advice to this day.

Linseed pours into a bowl.

An old vitamin bottle.

Books

This branch of the Talbots has produced a lot of clergymen, among them Benjamin and Jane's son Joseph, born in 1873, who grew up at Coole and married Dorothy Sophia White, the daughter of a wealthy Quaker merchant. Joseph went on to become the Right Reverend Dean of Cashel for 21 years while two of their sons were clergymen (Maurice, born in 1912, becoming Dean of Limerick in 1954).

(Raised as a Catholic myself, I never cease to be struck by the fact that when a Protestant becomes a member of the clergy, it has no potential impact on the family tree. In contrast, the ban on members of the Catholic clergy marrying can be substantial, sometimes to the point of causing the extinction of an entire branch of the family.)

Given the number of clergymen in the family it's no surprise to find numerous bibles in the house, ranging from the whopping leather-bound 7.65kg family bible in which the first birth entered on the family register therein is

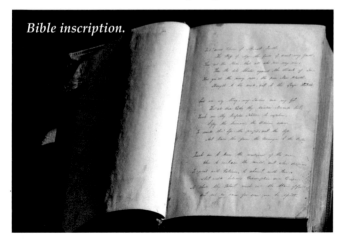

Bible inscription.

Benjamin Talbot, November 26th, 1871, to a 875g tiddling Red Letter New Testament in which the words of Jesus are printed in red ink, the inspiration for the style coming from Luke: "This cup is the new testament in my blood, which I shed for you."

Many of these volumes are well-used while others are fresh, including an Exposition of the old and new testaments in three volumes, with each volume running to some 1,500 pages. The first of these has a beautiful handwritten inscription. They were awarded as a Senior Sophister prize by Trinity College to the deliciously named Jacobo Henrico (James Henry) Bor.

A son of Humphrey Bor who built the new Ballindoolan House in Edenderry, Co Offaly, in 1822, he ministered in a number of parishes in Donegal. I was mystified for a long time as to his possible connection to the house until I discovered a plaque dedicated to his son Alfred Edward Bor on the wall of St Michael and All Angels church in the neighbouring parish of Abbeyleix where he was rector for over twenty years from 1898-1921. This made him a contemporary of Robin's grandfather Peter and his clergyman brothers Joseph and Robert.

There are numerous other religious works, including a series of hardback volumes from the mid-1850s entitled *The Sunday at Home – A Family Magazine for Sabbath Reading*, along with several books awarded as prizes for examinations in "Holy Scriptures & Church Formularies" and for Sunday School

NEAR ABBEYLEIX, QUEEN'S CO

attendance from well back into the 1800s.

Robin's gran-aunt, Frances, was a nurse and was recognised by the British Red Cross and the Order of St John of Jerusalem in England for her services during 1914-1919. Among the books here are, unsurprisingly, *A Textbook of War Nursing*, as well as some lighter reading such as a biography of English-born Fanny Jane Butler who was a pioneering doctor in India.

There is also a veterinary series, several farming books and some technical books including *Easy Lessons in Wireless*, a dog-eared series of which is interspersed with Walkers (playing) Card Reader. In an 1898 book entitled *South Africa*, items for sale include shooting helmets, mining machinery, pianos and "Shamrock Brand Sporting and Military Ammunition."

Most of the books, including a tattered set of

The New 20th Century Encyclopaedia, were published in London. There are also some housekeeping books (but none that I could find on cookery) interspersed with everything from sheet music, French, Latin and Intermediate examination schoolbooks such as one from 1887 entitled *The Hellenics of Xenophon*, and a range of novels such as *In the Palace of the King – A Love Story of Old Madrid*.

One of the most interesting books from a Laois point of view is *Leinster*, illustrated by Alexander Williams and described by Stephen Gwynn as part of a "beautiful" travel series from 1911-12. Dr Fiona MacGowan, an ecologist who lives locally, believes that the landscape described below is Raheen Bog. *(See picture on previous page).*

Such a scene as Mr Williams has drawn somewhere in the Queen's County is intensely typical of this midland county. Even where the furze blossom makes a flicker of gay colour, the whole effect is dismal, and its loneliness is constantly accentuated by what he has suggested, the flight of wild marsh-haunting birds: the trees are apt to be stunted and weather-twisted by winds off the "stormy Slieve Bloom", whose veiled purple shapes are shown against the western sky in his picture.

Yet the folk of this outer pale are "kindly Irish of the Irish" – none kindlier; and I have often thought the character of Ireland could not be better expressed than in a chance phrase I heard in the talk of a girl from that low-lying region. My father used always to tell me: 'Put plenty of potatoes in the pot, Maria. You couldn't tell who would be stepping in to us across the bog'.

The final paragraph of the book reads: "*Those who in visiting Ireland have too often found images and memories of beauty marred by the association of ragged poverty, overshadowed by a very cloud of despair, may find in Leinster at least a beauty where all the omens are hopeful and where, even beside the ruins only too evident, a strong new fabric of industry is being built up.*"

A selection of the bibles build up in the house over the years.

Old books tucked away in the store room.

Acknowledgements

So the journey of this book comes to an end. I hope you too, dear reader, have enjoyed your visit to our farm.

Before closing, I wish to express my gratitude to the many people who have seen this through to publication; to all who provided support, read, offered comments, allowed me to use their quotes and undertook the proof-reading, design and publishing. If anyone feels offended for not being mentioned I ask forgiveness.

In particular I would like to thank John McNamee of Laois Education Publishing and Eason Portlaoise who welcomed me from the first day I cold-called on him with little more than brass neck and an idea. In the interim he has provided me with a crash course in publishing along with no small amount of advice and encouragement. Also to PRINTcentral and Tommy Morrin for his endless patience, not to mention his skill and knowledge.

A number of professional colleagues from the world of agricultural journalism are now friends; among them Paddy Smith and Mairéad McGuinness MEP who, from the day she arrived as Editor of the *Farming Independent*, has always been an inspiration and when I asked her to write the Foreword she enthusiastically agreed.

Also the people profiled and photographed in this book, especially my mother-in-law Pam Talbot, close friends and family, including Sarah and Ruth who only occasionally (!) complained about being in "just one more shot", and also especially my late mother Rita who was selfless in her sacrifices to provide us with every opportunity.

Thanks to Archdeacon John Murray of Rathdowney Parish, genealogist Jane Lyons and Talbot relations Patrick Nicholson and Eileen Radelfinger for their help on the family tree. Dr Jack Carter not only provided historical background but also read the manuscript. He made a number of important suggestions which improved the tone of the text.

Also to Laois Partnership for their financial support, ecologists Fiona MacGowan and Mark McCorry who never tired of my emails seeking to identify some plant or bird, and Alf Harvey for selflessly sharing his boundless passion for, and knowledge of, photography.

Finally and, most importantly, to Robin, my husband, best friend and love of my life, my eternal thanks for his big heart, innovative spirit and sharp wit. He always makes me feel that I can achieve whatever I set my mind to.

Ann Talbot

Oak tree in mid-winter evening fog.

Ann Talbot (*nee* Fitzgerald) was born in 1964 and raised on a mixed farm in Ardagh, Co. Limerick. She worked for over 15 years as a freelance agricultural journalist (under her maiden name), writing for a number of publications including the Farming Independent where she was Livestock Editor for seven years, Farm Exam, Irish Field, Irish Farmers Journal and Meath Chronicle. She also reported widely on Point-to-Points, for Cork County Sound radio, Irish Independent and Cork (now Irish) Examiner.

She took a step back from writing when she became a mother and returns to journalism with this book.

Robin was born in 1957, left school after completing his Inter Cert and came home to farm in Coole, Ballacolla, Co Laois. He is an award-winning beef farmer and writes a monthly column for the Farming Independent.

They live with their daughters Sarah and Ruth and with Robin's mum, Pam.